POSITIVE ENERGY

HARNESSING PEOPLE POWER
TO PREVENT CLIMATE CHANGE

SIMON RETALLACK AND TIM LAWRENCE
WITH MATTHEW LOCKWOOD

ippr

The **Institute for Public Policy Research** is the UK's leading progressive think tank, producing cutting-edge research and innovative policy ideas for a just, democratic and sustainable world. Since 1988, we have been at the forefront of progressive debate and policymaking in the UK. Through our independent research and analysis we define new agendas for change and provide practical solutions to challenges across the full range of public policy issues. With offices in both London and Newcastle, we ensure our outlook is as broad-based as possible, while our international team and climate change programme extend our partnerships and influence beyond the UK, giving us a truly world-class reputation for high quality research.

For further information you can contact ippr's external affairs department on info@ippr.org, you can view our website at www.ippr.org and you can buy our books from Central Books on 0845 458 9910 or email ippr@centralbooks.com.

Our trustees

© IPPR 2007

CONTENTS

About the authors

Simon Retallack is head of the Climate Change Team at the Institute for Public Policy Research (ippr). He oversees ippr's Low Carbon Programme and was the lead researcher on the International Climate Change Taskforce project. Simon is also a board member of Redefining Progress, and an associate of the International Forum on Globalization. Previously, he was commissioning editor of *The Ecologist*. He is also the co-author of the prize-winning book *STOP* (with Laurent de Bartillat, Seuil, 2003).

Tim Lawrence was a research assistant in ippr's Sustainability Team, working on the Low Carbon Programme. Tim studied geography at the University of Bristol. With Tony Grayling and Tim Gibbs, he is the co-author of *Climate Commitment: Meeting the UK's 2010 CO2 emissions target* (ippr, 2005).

Matthew Lockwood is a Senior Research Fellow in ippr's Climate Change Team. He was environmental adviser to the Deputy Mayor of London and policy adviser to the London Climate Change Agency. Previously, Matthew was head of advocacy at ActionAid UK and head of international policy at Christian Aid.

Acknowledgements

We are very grateful for the financial support provided to ippr's public engagement project on climate change by the Energy Saving Trust, Pilkington Energy Efficiency Trust, RWE Npower and the core funders of ippr's two-year Low Carbon Programme: the Esmée Fairbairn Foundation, Shell International, CE Electric, the Ashden Trust and E.ON UK.

Special thanks are due to Gill Ereaut and Nat Segnit for their analysis of climate communications, to Greg Rowland, Virginia Valentine and Pat Dade for their help in developing new communications concepts, to Brian Samuel, Paul Chambers, Howard Reed, Miranda Lewis, Ian Kearns, Nick Pearce and Chris Powell for their comments on this report, as well as Chris Murray, Eleanor Stanley, Georgina Kyriacou, Jennifer Bird, John Schwartz, Kate English, Ruth Sheldon, Tatyana Eatwell, Tim Gibbs and Tony Grayling for their help and support at various points during the course of the project.

We would also particularly like to thank the following people for agreeing to take part in the advisory panel for this project, and for their invaluable advice: Brian Samuel (Energy Saving Trust), Graeme Trayner (Brunswick Group), Bryony Worthington (DEFRA), Chris Powell (BMP DDB), Solitaire Townsend (Futerra), Chris Rose (Campaign Strategies), David Watson (formerly Department for Transport), Lindsay Colbourne (Sustainable Development Commission), Mathew Davis (formerly WWF-UK), Gill Ereaut (Linguistic Landscapes), Pat Dade (Cultural Dynamics), Virginia Valentine (Semiotics Solutions), David Hone (Shell), Germana Canzi (formerly Friends of the Earth), Jon Bird (CE Electric), Matt Prescott (BBC) and Beth Tegg (Stop Climate Chaos).

Thanks also to the following people for agreeing to be consulted: Nick Eyre, Dan Staniaszek, Tim Curtis, Jon McGowan and Jennie Abelman (Energy Saving Trust), Tim Jackson (Surrey University), Ian Christie, Kate Dracup-Jones and Phillip Sivell (Surrey County Council), John Scott (ksbr), David Murphy (Department for Transport), Richard Ritchie, Andrew Mennear and John Wells (BP), John Leaman and Andrew Norton (MORI), Jonathon Shopley (Carbon Neutral Company), Jules Peck (Quality of Life Commission), Anthony Kleanhous, Andrea Kaszewski (WWF-UK), Russell Hamblin-Boone and Vance Duhaney (Energy Retail Association), Harriet Festing (Sustainable Development Commission), Ashok Sinha (Stop Climate Chaos), Steve Hounsham (Tomorrow's England), Peter Lipman and Melissa Henry (Sustrans), Dave Sowden (Micropower Council).

For their assistance in providing invaluable information and insight, our thanks to Jillian Anable (Robert Gordon University), Michael Buick and

Tom Morton (Climate Care), Alex Veitch, Kirk Archibald and Andrew Amato (Energy Saving Trust), Roger Webb (SBGI), Paul O'Hara, Eric Crane and James Purcell (Department for Transport), Louise Broom (Liftshare), Jane Kingswood (Carplus), Dawn Blackwell (Suffolk Car Share), Gloria Gabriel (MyLifts), and Julia Thomas (Transport 2000). Thanks also to E.ON, Scottish and Southern, Scottish Power and Manweb, Npower, EDF Energy, Ecotricity, Good Energy, Green Energy and British Gas for supplying information on the size of their green electricity markets.

Executive summary

Barely a week goes by without a press headline warning us of the dangers we face from climate change. Behind the stories, real people are already being hit, with climate change now killing 150,000 people a year.[1] The technological solutions to prevent it from becoming much worse already exist. The challenge is to make the transition to them in time to avoid dangerous climate change.

Some of the changes needed to make that transition will be achieved entirely through regulations that largely affect industry. Others will require individuals to choose to behave differently. In the UK, the energy we use in our homes and for personal transport is responsible for 44 per cent of the country's carbon dioxide (CO_2) emissions. Engaging with the public is therefore critical to reducing the country's overall contribution to climate change.

The challenge of doing so, however, is significant. A large proportion of the UK population is currently failing to take action to reduce their contribution despite high levels of awareness of the problem. In fact, the public is using an increasing amount of energy. Between 1990 and 2005, energy consumption rose by 40 per cent in the household sector, and by nearly 23 per cent in the transport sector.

Since 2001, national emissions have been growing too, and if the trend persists, the Government's target to reduce CO_2 emissions to 20 per cent below 1990 levels by 2010 will be missed by a substantial margin. Over the coming decades, the challenge will be even greater. Without the acceptance, support and active participation of the public, the UK's chances of reaching its target of reducing CO_2 emissions by 60 per cent below 1990 levels by 2050 will be very low.

Engaging the public in this way will not only benefit the climate: helping individuals to use energy more efficiently and be less reliant on fossil fuels will also help government meet its other energy policy objectives of increasing energy security and reducing fuel poverty. More broadly, empowering people to exert control and resolve problems for themselves is a good in its own right: improving governance, deepening democracy and rebuilding trust.

When it comes to climate change, there is clear evidence that members of the public who are concerned about this issue do not always feel

---

1   References for all the facts and figures cited in this summary can be found in the main report.

engaged in the societal challenge of tackling it, and feel locked into the systems and norms that fuel it. There is an urgent need to enable people such as these to act to reduce their contribution. The aim of this report is to find more effective ways of doing so.

Based on an extensive, cross-disciplinary literature review, interviews and a discourse analysis of UK climate change communications, this report suggests policies, techniques and communications approaches for promoting behaviour change. It is intended to help policymakers and others seeking to reduce the public's contribution to climate change to do so as effectively as possible.

Which behaviours need changing?

Almost 60 per cent of the contribution of an average UK citizen to CO_2 comes from using energy in the home. Of these emissions, three quarters come from heating space and water alone (the single largest contributor to emissions by individuals in a given year), and one quarter from powering refrigerators, lights, ovens, washing and dishwashing machines, and consumer electronics.

Changes that will do the most to reduce individuals' CO_2 emissions from home energy use include fitting insulation in cavity walls and loft spaces, installing an efficient condensing boiler, and installing micro-renewable technology for heat (such as solar thermal and biomass) and electricity.

The remaining 40 per cent of an average UK citizen's contribution to CO_2 comes from transport, including flying. Almost three quarters of this can be attributed to car use, with almost a quarter coming from flying.

Consequently, changes that will do most to reduce individuals' transport emissions include cycling, walking, using public transport, buying lower-carbon cars (such as those with smaller or hybrid engines, or that use bio-fuels), and driving more efficiently ('eco-driving'). Flying less, by taking holidays nearer to home or by train, or offsetting flights effectively, will also help.

People can also affect climate change through less direct means, such as purchasing food and consumer products that have been made using less energy and transported smaller distances, or taking part in campaigning to encourage decision-makers to take action on climate change. Each of these is a legitimate, and potentially valuable, avenue of individual action.

However, in most cases it is still very difficult to assess accurately the significance of such actions. As a result, this report focuses mainly on those changes in behaviour relating to energy use in the home and in transport, whose contribution to climate change through emissions can be easily measured.

What is the public doing about climate change?

It is clear from the evidence that the majority of people in the UK are not taking many actions to mitigate their emissions in a significant way.

A large number of homes are still not properly insulated. Almost two thirds (63 per cent) of homes that could have cavity-wall insulation – some 8.3 million homes – have not installed it. Similarly, in 2003, 48 per cent of homes that could have had loft insulation fitted at the optimum depth (4 inches) did not do so.

Since 2005 it has been mandatory to fit the most efficient type of condensing boiler. However, there are a further 15 million that need to be replaced. Homes are also kept appreciably warmer than they were 30 years ago: between 1990 and 2004 there was a rise of 1.9°C in internal temperatures.

While people do increasingly buy energy-efficiency A-rated appliances, the energy savings from doing so have been more than offset by the 50 per cent growth in the number of appliances in the home between 1990 and 2004 – especially in consumer electronics. Exacerbating the problem further, some new products consume more electricity than the products they replace (for example, plasma televisions consume 4.5 times more energy than their cathode ray tube predecessors).

By contrast, investment in micro-renewables is still a tiny niche market, as is 'green' tariff electricity (electricity that energy companies have produced from renewable sources of energy). There are currently only around 100,000 microgeneration installations in the UK, representing under 0.4 per cent of UK households. And just 212,000 customers have switched to a green electricity tariff, representing some 0.83 per cent of the total electricity market in 2005.

A similar picture exists for transport choices. People are using their cars to travel further, and more often, with an 18.5 per cent increase in the number of vehicle kilometres by cars and taxis since 1990. Car ownership is also increasing: there were nearly one third more cars on UK roads in 2005 than in 1990 – equivalent to another 7.5 million more cars.

Although there has been an increase in public transport use, it still makes up only 8 per cent of the total number of trips made. Only London has seen a shift away from car use to buses and an increase in cycling. Outside of the capital, local bus use has declined on average by almost 12 per cent since 1990. Nationally, cycling represents only 1.5 per cent of all journeys made and the distance travelled and number of trips taken by bicycle have fallen by 6 and 20 per cent respectively. Participation in car clubs and car-share schemes remains a niche choice.

The one area of positive change is that average emissions from the nation's car fleet are coming down. However, this is largely being driven by technology rather than by consumer behaviour. In 2005, total sales of low-carbon vehicles (LCVs), which are mostly hybrid cars, amounted to just 0.3 per cent of the market.

Meanwhile, few motorists recognise the concept of driving more efficiently. Data from average vehicle speeds on motorways shows that a majority (56 per cent) of cars exceed the 70 miles per hour speed limit, with more than one third of drivers exceeding 80 miles per hour.

Lastly, air travel is now more popular than ever, and offsetting remains a small minority practice. Between 1994 and 2004 the number of passengers flying abroad from the UK rose by about 65 per cent, and the number flying domestically by about 70 per cent. According to a 2006 poll, just 1–5 per cent of respondents said they offset their emissions from flying.

What are the attitudes of the public towards climate change?

Why is it that the behaviour of individuals in the UK is currently not 'climate friendly'? The most recent surveys show that more than 90 per cent of respondents accept that climate change is happening, and a majority see it as the result of human action. Most are also worried about climate change, with 77 per cent of respondents in one survey saying that they were very, or fairly, concerned about the issue, with just 23 per cent not very, or not at all, concerned. Equally, a large majority of people surveyed (76 to 90 per cent) in two recent polls stated that they believed climate change will affect the UK, and a majority of the public now associates extreme weather events with climate change.

However, despite this widespread concern, most people are unaware of how they are contributing to the problem (with many, for example, uninformed of the impact of domestic energy use) or what practical steps they can take to mitigate it.

The public acknowledges that it makes some contribution to the problem. In a recent government survey, over 70 per cent of people accepted that they personally contributed to the production of CO_2 emissions and thus climate change. But they said they did not believe that they had a responsibility to act to reduce their contribution, and just 7 per cent felt they personally could influence it to a large extent. Far too many say there is little they can do about climate change themselves.

The locus of responsibility is still frequently assigned to government, industry and other countries. There is also a wariness of 'free riders', and a felt need for everyone to play their part. According to a 2005 Eurobarometer poll, of those who are making an effort to protect the environment, 61 per cent do not feel their efforts will have any impact as long as other citizens or corporations and industry do not do the same. Those who do not take environmental action use this same reason as justification for continuing not to do so.

There are mixed results on unilateral action within the UK. In a 2006 survey, some 52 per cent believed that climate change will happen regardless of what we do in Britain. By contrast, other surveys show some support for the view that trying to tackle climate change is worthwhile, even without global agreement.

Many key public attitudes towards climate change should not be surprising. The worst impacts of climate change are distant in space and time, its direct causes (in other words, emissions) are invisible, and we are all responsible for producing them. Everyone seeks to be a free rider because it is in everyone's interest for others to take on the costs of acting as the individual will benefit from those actions while avoiding the costs of acting themselves.

Equally, climate change provides perfect conditions for the 'bystander effect', whereby there is mass paralysis when people are confronted with a problem but do not act because they think others should, and will. Defence mechanisms in the face of a threat perceived to be 'uncontrollable' are also likely to be at work here – notably, fatalism and seeking scapegoats. Clearly, public attitudes towards taking action are also justifications for the defence of lifestyles to which people are strongly attached and perceive to be under threat.

Are communications about climate change helping or hindering change?

Much of what people think about climate change is influenced by how the issue is communicated to them. The mass media plays a key role, as this is where most people get their information on social issues from, but other actors, such as the Government, public bodies, non-governmental organisations (NGOs) and companies, also play an important role in communicating about and providing information on climate change.

ippr commissioned experts to analyse communications from each of these sources, using tools and principles of discourse analysis and semiotics, to assess whether existing communications on climate change in the UK were helping or hindering efforts to achieve behaviour change. They identified several 'linguistic repertoires' – systems of language that are routinely used for making sense about climate change and our response to it. These fall into three groups:

- the alarmism repertoire
- the sceptical set of repertoires, which assume 'it'll be all right'
- the pragmatic set of repertoires, which assume 'it'll be all right as long as we do something.'

Climate change is most commonly talked about using the alarmism repertoire, which describes climate change as awesome, terrible and immense, with implications that it is beyond human control. This repertoire is seen almost everywhere, and is used across the ideological spectrum, in broadsheet and tabloid newspapers, popular magazines and campaign literature from government and environmental groups. It is clearly disempowering, carrying the sub-text that 'things are so bad that we might as well give up and carry on emitting'.

In contrast, the underlying message of the two remaining sets of repertoires is that, despite all the fuss about climate change, everything will be all right.

In the sceptical set of repertoires, arguments are found that state either that man-made climate change is simply not happening at all, or that we need not worry about its consequences. Their underlying message is that there is no need to change behaviour. These repertoires are most clearly and commonly seen in the right-wing press.

The pragmatic set of repertoires contains the underlying message that everything will be all right as long as we do something. The most significant approach within these repertoires focuses on 'small actions'. This involves a large number of people doing small things to counter climate change (such as turning down thermostats, not leaving televisions on standby, and buying efficient light bulbs). The language conveys ease, convenience and effortless agency, as well as domesticity. The problem with this approach is that it easily lapses into 'wallpaper' – the domestic, the routine, the boring, and the too easily ignored.

The two most dominant approaches within the UK dialogue are the alarmism repertoire, and the 'small actions' repertoire, within the pragmatic set. Both these approaches are frequently paired, with headlines such as '20 small things you can do to save the planet from destruction'. This has been seen in many popular magazine features and government-funded campaigns.

The problem with this combination is that in the end, it is not convincing. The juxtaposition of the awesome scale of climate change in alarmism and the small, mundane responses in the 'small actions' discourse implicitly raises the question of how the latter can really make a difference to things happening on this epic scale. The question is left unanswered, and the public is not motivated enough to act.

What are the other barriers to behaviour change?

As we have seen, there is an absence of a compelling story on climate change within current communications, and a lack of a strong public sense of responsibility and agency for taking action. These are combined with a host of other factors that explain why people do not take up new climate-friendly behaviours. Many of the barriers are closely interlinked and involve a combination of a range of practical problems, as well as a number of psychological and social factors that prevent change.

With energy use in the home, the status quo is perpetuated by the invisibility of energy use, by the desire for warm, bright, convenient and entertaining homes, and by engrained day-to-day habits. On the other hand, conservation measures largely fail to bring any personal benefit in terms of social status and emotional fulfilment, and only relatively marginal cost savings for most households. They suffer from a poor image, are perceived to involve high upfront capital costs (lifetime costs and discounts are ignored), and take time to organise and inconvenience to be installed – particularly as suppliers are not trusted.

Microgeneration technologies suffer from being seen as unfamiliar and eccentric. There are common misconceptions about their effectiveness, and it can be time-consuming to find out about relevant products and install them. But the single most significant barrier to their uptake is the high capital cost, with the unacceptably long payback periods this implies. In urban areas, micro-wind payback periods are of the order of 10–15 years, while for solar photovoltaics (PV) they can be longer than 30 years. This cost problem is compounded by the fact that it is still difficult to get a fair reward for any exported electricity and related Renewable Obligation certificates.[2]

The status quo with regards to car use is perpetuated by people's strong attachment to the car, based partly on the way it is associated with social status, and with an ability to shape identity, and its perceived superiority over alternatives in terms of independence, convenience, comfort, safety, and cost. Meanwhile, lower-carbon cars suffer from image problems, misconceptions about performance, higher upfront cost than their equivalents and, for certain technologies, a lack of infrastructure.

Finally, cutting back on flying is resisted because of people's aspiration and sense of entitlement to holiday abroad rather than in the UK, the higher social status associated with doing so, the desire to travel further than before for increasingly exotic holidays, and to take shorter but more frequent trips. In those circumstances, flying is the most convenient form of travel, given its speed, and has become much more affordable as the cost of flying has fallen significantly. Offsetting, meanwhile, is hampered by low awareness of the option and, where knowledge of it does exist, a lack of belief that it is meaningful.

---

2   These are currently issued to qualifying renewables generators as evidence that a licensed electricity supplier has supplied renewable electricity to their customers in Great Britain. These certificates can then be presented or bought by electricity suppliers to count towards meeting their targets under the Renewables Obligation to source an increasing proportion of the electricity they sell from renewables.

Has the traditional approach to behaviour change worked?

How can government and others most effectively intervene to remove the barriers people face? Historically, in trying to change public behaviour, governments have tended to rely on two main approaches – sending price signals and providing information. Both have been preferred over direct regulation or coercion, as this is expensive politically and financially, as well as being unworkable for some behaviours.

The use of these levers to change behaviour has been based largely on the 'rational choice' model of human behaviour, according to which humans behave in a way that rationally maximises their welfare. They do this by making systematic use of the information available to them and assessing the choices before them in terms of costs and benefits. However, this approach has had limited success.

It is true that providing more information about environmental problems has been shown to be one factor in acting pro-environmentally, but on its own, this approach has frequently failed to translate into behaviour change. Indeed, in some cases, it has been a change in behaviour that has caused a change in attitudes. In other situations, providing information that is not accompanied by measures enabling people to act may have been counterproductive, by making people feel helpless.

The use of taxes and subsidies to discourage – or encourage – behaviours has a rather better track record, as people's decisions are sometimes swayed by cost. The switch to unleaded petrol and the London congestion charge are two examples in which changing prices through tax has led to a shift in behaviour. But once again, evidence suggests that price signals alone are rarely sufficient. In some cases, because other factors are more influential in determining behaviours than rational calculations about cost, price fails to stimulate behaviour change at all. Gas and electricity use in the home, for example, has hardly changed in response to the large price increases over the last two years.

The limitations of the 'rational choice' approach for public policy can be clearly seen in the poor performance of some of the interventions designed solely on that basis. It is increasingly recognised within the cognitive sciences that individual rationality is profoundly embedded in, and dependent on, the individual's wider social environment and psychology. Until very recently, this more complex view has not been taken fully into account in designing policy.

What is the Government doing to change climate-related behaviours?

Over the past ten years, the Government has relied largely on the traditional tools for influencing climate-related behaviour: regulation, price incentives and information.

The most consistent element of government policy has been creating incentives. There has been price support for insulation and other domestic energy-efficiency measures through the £400 million a year Energy Efficiency Commitment programme (plus fuel poverty programmes), along with value-added tax (VAT) reductions. There has also been grant support for microgeneration. In addition, along with fuel duty, there have been variable tax policies to push people towards lower-carbon cars, with banded Vehicle Excise Duty (VED), as well as support for alternative fuels. Finally, to reduce flying, the Government raised Air Passenger Duty (APD) in December 2006.

The limited impact of these measures on behaviour is partly due to the fact that they have been rather cautious, combined with a very low effective price of carbon. For example, differential taxation through VED at current levels is too small to make a significant difference to behaviour, and small APD increases make little difference in a market where ticket costs have plummeted. Where a shift in behaviour does take place – for example, in the rising demand for micro-renewables – the scale of the resources provided by the Government (a mere £6 million initially for domestic microgeneration) cannot cope.

Government has used regulation to force behaviour change only in a limited way – for example through building regulations – and where incentives or voluntary agreements have failed. There is often a preference for schemes with manufacturers or energy suppliers (for example, with the Energy Efficiency Commitment, or the Renewable Fuels Obligation to introduce biofuels) that bypass the need to engage actively with the public.

Recent government leadership has been stronger in terms of the goals guiding the practices and procurement policies of government departments, although even here the record is patchy. But its broader policies – particularly in relation to transport, where there is clear backing for airport expansion and a new £1.9 billion road-building programme – have not always been consistent with the need to send a clear public signal about the importance of acting to reduce emissions.

The Government's own communications campaigns on climate have mainly been focused on changing attitudes to open up the political space for mitigation policies, rather than on behaviour change directly. This is now set to change, with a new (though somewhat cautious) series of campaigns starting in 2007. However, there remain significant gaps in the provision of practical information to the public on climate-friendly behaviour, and it remains sobering that the main government vehicle for communicating such information (the Energy Saving Trust) is contacted by only 3 per cent of the public in any one year.

What actually shapes behaviour?

Clearly, a great deal more needs to be done to overcome the barriers to behaviour change. To be more effective, policy needs to take into account the diverse and complex range of influences on behaviour, which should lead to the pursuit of a much greater range of options for action.

Decades of theoretical development and empirical research from different disciplines – ranging from psychology and anthropology to economics – have given us a much clearer idea of how, and why, behaviour changes. Some of the factors that drive behaviours are internal to an individual, while others are external. These internal and external factors feed off and influence each other, which means that behaviour is often best interpreted from an 'ecological' perspective that meshes personal factors with wider structural and social ones.

Policymakers have been relatively good at working with some internal influences on behaviour, such as wealth and age, as well as with some external influences, such as financial rewards and penalties. They also understand that the choices they make about which rules and infrastructure to put in place are very influential. But much more could be done to factor in other influences.

Important internal influences that need to be taken into account include:

- different psychological motivations (as defined, for example, by Abraham Maslow's 'hierarchy of human needs')
- the drive to seek status and forge identities
- emotions
- habits
- mental shortcuts used to decide how to act (combining pieces of information together and using rules to make decisions faster and more easily)
- a sense of responsibility and agency to act differently.

Important external influences that need to be factored in include:

- the behaviour and attitudes of others (noting that we do not learn equally from everyone)
- the dominant social and cultural norms (often shaped by the media and commercial organisations), which give us social proof about how to behave
- the nature of the experiences that people have (evidence suggests direct experiences are more powerful than indirect ones)
- any rewards and penalties (both financial and other) that are in place.

With a more complete understanding of how and why people behave the way they do, we stand a much better chance of deploying the most effective tools and techniques available to achieve behaviour change.

How has behaviour change been achieved?

The history of social and technological change in the 20th century shows that it is possible for people's behaviours to change completely – including some of the most harmful ones – even in the space of just a few years. We now know much more about how such change can be achieved. There is no single silver bullet. But critical to a successful approach is the deployment of interventions that work with, or on, the main internal and external drivers of behaviour.

Often, the most important first step is to provide people with alternatives that are convenient and affordable, since their capacity to act is often constrained by the amount of free time and money they have. We also know the importance of making sure that alternatives at least appear to be affordable, by providing ways of spreading any upfront costs over time. This is because of the mental shortcuts that people take, which mean that they are affected more by losses than gains, and discount the future and any delayed benefits from change.

Asking people to make public commitments to change (and deploying prompts to remind them to do so) can work, by raising people's consciousness about habitual behaviours. Publicly made commitments can also increase people's sense of responsibility for changing their behaviour.

Giving people feedback on attempts to change behaviour, providing face-to-face engagement, and involving people in group-level change can also increase their sense of agency, as participants can see and evaluate the impact of their efforts and are given direct, personal support to alter their behaviour.

A sense of agency from group-based engagement can be deepened by drawing people into participatory problem solving. This approach has taken off in the health field, where a new generation of interventions aimed at changing behaviour through greater patient participation in the delivery of services has been used to effect change in a range of situations, from managing diabetes to increasing mobility among older people.

Once alternatives, awareness, and a sense of responsibility are in place, then incentives, rewards and penalties are much more likely to work. Rewards do not have to involve cash: they can range from football tickets to meal vouchers or IT training. What is important is their appeal to the individual, their tangible, short-term benefit, and their visibility.

The impact of what others are doing around us is also very powerful. Interventions to create exemplars of change among figures of influence or colleagues in the workplace, and in the wider community, can help create new social norms that can have a significant impact on individual behaviour.

Another element of effective behaviour change is communication. Communication alone will not change behaviour, but it can play a role in complementing and reinforcing other interventions – especially where it is linked to specific behaviour changes and spells out what people can do, how, why, where and when. The history of commercial marketing points to another important pre-condition – the imperative to know and segment one's audience, not only along socio-economic lines, but also by psychological motivations.

Given what we know about the role of emotion, status seeking and the construction of identity in behaviour, the 'communication hooks' themselves must have emotional appeal and should make behaviour changes appear aspirational. They also need to take account of the mental shortcuts or frames that people use to make sense of incoming information, and to accept or reject it, which shapes how they react. Concepts, language and images need to be chosen accordingly. Lastly, repetition, staying power and, above all, consistency can make the difference between a successful campaign and an unsuccessful one.

The challenge for government and others seeking to change behaviour through public engagement is to recognise and embrace this full range of psychosocial approaches. Conventional policies are still important, but, as parts of government are increasingly recognising, the policy palette must be widened to successfully stimulate climate-friendly behaviour.

Recommendations: a new approach to stimulating climate-friendly behaviour

Getting people to change their climate-related behaviours requires a deeper understanding of what shapes these behaviours in the first place. Government is beginning to engage with this agenda, but to be successful, it needs to confront an array of deep-seated issues in a way that only a systematic, strategic approach can achieve.

There are four essential elements to such an approach:

- prioritising the areas where behaviour needs to change
- identifying which are the key barriers in the priority areas, and which groups of people are particularly involved
- developing the most appropriate interventions to overcome those barriers
- developing smart and effective communications.

To illustrate how the framework can be applied, we propose our own suggestions for prioritising behaviours to change, largely according to their contribution to carbon emissions. Our target behaviour changes include those needed to reduce emissions from:

- domestic heating and hot water
- driving
- flying.

Together, these account for almost 85 per cent of measurable emissions from activities by individuals. Among the associated behaviour changes, we include installing micro-renewables, since this is potentially a high-status behaviour change that could act as a catalyst for further changes.

With each of the areas identified as priorities, government will seek to maximise the use of interventions that do not require behaviour change at all. But this will still leave a large proportion of the problem in the hands of the individual, who will need to actively choose to behave differently.

How the interventions might be applied

The following proposals provide examples of how psychosocial interventions might be applied in parallel with more traditional approaches to overcome barriers to achieving those changes. They present a range of possible options for government to consider, rather than a comprehensive list or road-map. Policymakers would need to cost them, sequence them carefully, and in some cases, trial them before implementing them on a national scale.

The specific proposals are detailed below, set out within the three priority areas identified above: domestic heating and hot water, car use, and flying. These three categories are then subdivided into types of specific activity.

Domestic heating and hot water (including micro-renewables)
Raising understanding
- Require energy companies to check customers' meters at least twice a year and put more information on their bills to allow them to compare their energy use and CO_2 impact over time.
- Draw up plans to start a five-year UK-wide programme to roll out the installation of smart meters and real-time feedback displays, from 2007.
- Explore ways of ensuring each UK home is given an energy audit by 2012, and train more auditors – possibly through the Energy Saving Trust or a new agency.
- Target accurate and authoritative information on energy-efficiency and microgeneration products at the building trade, architects and the public.
- Consider establishing an authoritative micro-renewables accreditation body to set standards and certify the performance of microgeneration technologies.

Improving image
- Support 'green home makeover' services to roll dull energy measures into a wider 'green home' package with aspirational appeal.
- Work to build up celebrity support for domestic energy saving and microgeneration to rival that for Prius cars.

- Set up product design competitions for real-time energy feedback devices, micro-renewables, and traditional products that are hard to sell, such as external wall insulation.

Social proofing[3]
- Set every government department a target to source 10 per cent of its energy from on-site renewables by 2010, and encourage city governments to promote flagship renewables projects.
- Explore ways of providing the funding necessary for every school to have an appropriate form of on-site renewable energy generation by 2015, as part of the major school rebuilding programme Schools for the Future.
- Extend this approach to other public buildings, such as those managed by health trusts, by expanding funding for civic leadership through the Low Carbon Buildings Programme.

Setting attractive rewards
- Explore ways of rolling out council-tax rebates for energy-efficiency measures nationwide.
- Require energy utilities to provide technology-specific feed-in tariffs for micro-renewables at a fair rate (following the lead of many European Union member states).
- Examine the possibility of allowing householders investing in micro-generation to claim 100 per cent enhanced capital allowances against tax. (This allowance could be phased out as the market matures.)

Increasing affordability
- Significantly expand the grant support programme for microgeneration, and take measures to make sure there are no funding gaps in future.
- Consider mandating on-site renewable generation for all new housing to reduce capital costs by achieving greater economies of scale.
- Work with the European Union to allow reduced VAT on 'do-it-yourself' insulation products.
- Introduce an obligation on suppliers to reduce energy sold, in place of the current Energy Efficiency Commitment (EEC), by 2008 – or at least make the third phase of EEC (running from 2008-11) a transition towards it – to incentivise energy suppliers to finance large energy-efficiency investments through on-bill repayments of capital costs.
- Create incentives for banks and building societies to offer 'green' mortgages and loans to cover the capitals costs of energy-efficiency work done on a house, to install microgeneration systems.

---

3   Social proofing refers to the process of taking steps to normalise measures to reduce emissions so that the 'social proof' about how to behave can be found all around us.

Ensuring group support
- Expand financial support for initiatives such as Global Action Plan's 'eco-teams', so that most households have access to one within five years.
- Set up an agency to provide technical advice to community groups – particularly to ensure successful initiatives are replicated.

Providing convenience
- Support the development of a 'hand-holding' project-management service that removes from householders the hassle and risk of organising and installing insulation and micro-renewables.

Committing to change
- Consider tasking energy auditors to ask householders to sign a written but voluntary commitment to implement some or all of the recommendations made.
- Alternatively, explore the possibility of requiring all UK homes at the point of sale (and possibly even rented properties) to meet minimum energy performance standards. (The new Energy Performance Certificate could be the first step towards such an approach.)

Car use
Providing convenience
- Subject all new transport spending to an emissions assessment before funding is given, and prioritise investment in affordable, high quality and convenient public transport – particularly bus services.
- Increase support for better cycle lanes, more and better shower and parking facilities at work and in public places, and cycle-hire facilities at stations, working with local authorities to ensure that this takes place.
- Establish and fund a national forum for sharing good practice around the country in bus services, 'bus taxis', and measures to promote cycling, walking, car clubs, car-share services, and remote working.
- Build the requirement for high-density mixed-use development into the planning system at all levels, and reject any easing of restrictions on out-of-town developments that create more car trips.
- Explore scaling-up the existing programme to provide support for alternative refuelling stations to provide nationwide coverage rapidly.

Raising understanding
- Explore ways of facilitating a national rollout of personalised travel planning to all households in urban areas of England over a ten-year period.
- Improve the flexibility of Local Transport Plan funding so that it sup-

ports travel plans (see previous recommendation) and not only capital projects.

- Task the Carbon Trust to advise and assist all businesses in developing work travel plans, to match those for schools.
- Run an open competition – including in schools – for the design of stickers and other prompts to remind people to break their car habit and use alternatives instead, for use in the home and car. Distribute winning designs through supermarkets, newspapers, environmental NGOs and Global Action Plan groups.
- Make emissions-related car labelling mandatory for all new car sales.

Improving image
- Work to secure celebrity endorsements for public transport, cycling and walking, and step up the celebrity endorsement of lower-carbon vehicles such as the Toyota Prius – especially from public figures with high visibility with motorists, such as Premiership footballers.
- Organise a design competition for desirable buses and trains through the Design Council, involving the major franchisees on rail and bus routes.
- Take the lead within Europe in getting car companies to sign up to a code of good advertising practice by mid-2007, so that as with health warnings on tobacco products, all car advertising carries bold and visible warnings about the contribution of driving to climate change.

Social proofing
- Make additional funding available to those local authorities (including public transport franchises), health trusts and emergency services that adopt a target for reducing emissions from transport that is at least as ambitious as central Government's, to help them meet this target through a mixture of managing demand and procuring low-carbon vehicles.
- Ensure that ministers and MPs keep travel diaries, posted on appropriate websites, showing their use of buses, trains, cycling and walking.

Setting attractive rewards and repellent penalties
- Introduce a Vehicle Excise Duty (VED) escalator for the higher-band cars, and freeze or further reduce taxation of the lower bands. Over time, aim for differentials of £300 per band.
- Examine the option of a subsidy to employers located at the edge of cities or on industrial parks to encourage shuttle buses for staff – possibly financed by an increase in company car tax for high CO_2 emission bands.
- Commit to a policy of national road pricing and, if VED is cut as a result, impose a similar emissions-based banding system on the scheme, accompanied by increased investments in public transport.

Increasing affordability
- Explore the possibility of using revenues from steeper VED charges for higher bands to finance the restoration of the Government's programme of technology-neutral subsidies for the purchase of low-carbon vehicles for five years.
- Find ways of supporting loan finance packages for the purchase of low-carbon vehicles through a topping-up provision, to be phased out over five years as the market matures, similar to the proposed support for green mortgages (see above).

Committing to change
- Encourage commitments to make lower-carbon journeys to work, through workplaces, and through local community groups for all types of journeys, using the individualised travel-marketing home visits process described above to encourage people to commit to action on a voluntary basis.
- Incentivise city governments and local authorities to offer formal contracts for changing travel behaviour, combined with the provision of attractive alternatives and incentives (such as free tickets and bicycles).

Flying
Decreasing affordability
- Over time, increase a reformed Air Passenger Duty (APD) in real terms.
- Continue to press for reform of the international convention governing taxation of aviation fuel, and for effective terms for including aviation in the EU Emissions Trading Scheme, including full auctioning and tight caps.

Providing convenience
- Explore the possibility of matching any increase in APD with expanded support for investment in rail – especially to increase rail capacity and expand high-speed rail networks.
- Work with other EU member states to reform the currently fragmented European rail network, replacing it with a seamless EU-wide service, with simple timetabling and cheapness to rival flying.

Improving image
- Work with train operators to make rail travel aspirational, with celebrity endorsement and targeted marketing.
- Support investment in a more radical refitting and rebuilding of bus and train stations to make them fit for 21st-century (rather than 19th-century) travel.
- Consider providing more funding to market the UK as an enticing holiday destination that is easily reached without all the cost and hassle of flying.

Raising understanding
- Require all advertising for air travel and holiday packages that involves flying to carry bold, highly visible warnings about the contribution of flying to climate change. Similar warnings should be displayed at all UK airports.
- Make the Government's voluntary code of best practice for offsetting a mandatory standard, and require all airlines to offer passengers the chance to opt out (rather than to opt in) to offsetting schemes.

Social proofing
- Set new, climate-friendly travel guidelines for ministers and officials.
- Encourage other high-profile individuals in society to make public pledges not to fly, or to reduce their flying.
- Task the Carbon Trust to ensure that companies and public bodies adopt travel policies for employees that encourage a responsible approach to flying.
- Increase support for local mutual support groups in which members can set themselves goals or commitments to reduce their flying, as well as monitor and provide feedback on their own progress.
- Stop provision for the mass expansion of the UK's national airports so that efforts to create new social norms on flying are not undermined.

Smart and effective communications
- Lead on and fund a higher-profile, larger-scale, long-running national communications campaign on climate change, to run once the other kinds of policy interventions suggested above are adopted. This should be carried out in partnership with the private sector, the Energy Saving Trust and campaigning groups, with an initial financial commitment of at least £8 million per year for five years.
- Ensure that the primary focus of this campaign should not be on the problem but on the large-scale solutions that people can take and the impact these can have.
- Give the campaign an overarching brand under which different sub-messages appear over time, involving specific requests for the public to change specific behaviours.
- Make people feel that they can make these changes, and would want to do so, by making them appear desirable, while telling them how.
- For each targeted behaviour, test and establish exactly what should be communicated, how, to whom, using which messengers, and through which channels, through properly funded research with the public. Throughout the campaign, test and adapt the strategy using focus groups and deliberative workshops.
- Complement existing segmentation of the population by socio-economic or lifestyle group with psychographic models, allowing the moti-

vations of particular groups to be more effectively tapped into.
- Make sure the campaign uses the 'strategic frame' analysis to deploy language relating to the higher-level values subscribed to by target audiences.
- Ensure the Government's own practices and policies (particularly on transport) are consistent with what it is asking the public to do at all times.

A new partnership

Although these recommendations are aimed at central government, the agenda set out here may be delivered through local government, community groups, eco-auditors working for civil society organisations, social enterprises and, indeed, large corporations. National government can clearly help by promoting initiatives led by these players, and by providing them with dependable funding streams. It might even consider setting up community groups itself, to deliver services on the ground.

At the same time, government itself must also remain visible. People look to government to take a lead, so it must be clear in all these different forms of delivery and engagement that government is playing the lead role.

A systematic and strategic approach also calls for a new centralised unit for climate-friendly behaviour change to be set up in Whitehall. This unit would be tasked with auditing all government policy to establish shortcomings, recommend improvements, and ensure a strategic and coordinated approach exists to stimulating climate-friendly behaviour across government. The unit should also engage with the public, as partners in the co-creation of policy through deliberative events. The unit could be housed in the Government Office of Climate Change, but it should work closely with the Government's current main delivery agency for behaviour change – the Energy Saving Trust.

The programmes of the Energy Saving Trust (EST) itself should be given expanded and dependable funding into the future so that the EST can increase its capacity to support the public in adopting climate-friendly behaviour. Any such additional funding should be conditional on an assessment of the EST's effectiveness, and its adoption of the direction of travel outlined in this report.

Conclusions

The options outlined in this report are driven not only by appeals to the rational side of human nature, but also by a range of social and psychological factors. Some of them will prove fruitful, while others may not. But government urgently needs to begin considering them seriously. If we fail to use this palette of options to change behaviours in a significant way in the next few years, we may have to fall back on yet more radical (and possibly more costly) policy options, such as carbon rationing for individuals.

Before change on this scale is imposed, people deserve the right to be given the possibility to change. A growing proportion of the public is clearly concerned about the climate problem, and good policy will dictate that they should be empowered to do something about it themselves. Exhortations to behave differently will not work. Approaches to enable people to adopt alternative forms of behaviour, by making them cheaper, more visible and more attractive, are now urgently needed. Then the positive energy that people acting together can bring to bear may truly be harnessed to beat this problem.

Introduction

'We have to accept that cutting domestic emissions is not a responsibility for Government alone... We can and will encourage changes in behaviour. In the end... combating climate change will be a responsibility for every one of us.'

Tony Blair (2006)

'Environmental protection needs... a new contract between empowered and responsible citizens and empowering and responsive governments.'

Gordon Brown (2007)

Barely a week now goes by without a press headline warning us of the dangers we face from climate change. Recent examples include: 'Hottest year on record in Northern Hemisphere', 'Greenhouse gases reach highest level for 650,000 years', 'Levels of Arctic sea ice at record low' and 'Intense hurricanes become twice as common'.

Behind the barrage of stories, real people – and their homes and businesses – are already being hit. Climate change is killing 150,000 people a year, according to the World Health Organization, through increased heatwaves, floods, storms, droughts and the spread of water- and insect-borne diseases (WHO 2005).

The reinsurer Munich Re warns that the economic losses from weather-related disasters reached a record US$200 billion in 2005 with Hurricane Katrina, which was the single most expensive insured event in history, costing insurers over US$30 billion (UNEP 2005a). Climate change is also damaging the planet's precious natural ecosystems, including the world's coral reefs, which are dying as oceans warm.

The cause of the problem is known, and the technological solutions to prevent it from becoming much worse already exist. Fundamentally, the solution will require replacing our old and inefficient system of generating energy – a system that burns coal, oil and gas, producing heat-trapping gases – with a new system that requires a lot less energy in the first place, and produces the rest cleanly.

The challenge is to achieve that transition quickly enough. Research suggests that to have a high chance of preventing dangerous climate change, global emissions of the main greenhouse gas, carbon dioxide (CO_2), will need to be reduced by 70–80 per cent by the middle of the century (Baer and Mastrandrea 2006).

The need for public engagement

So far, much of the official focus has fallen on the role of industry in meeting that challenge. The companies that produce energy, the industrial and business consumers of that energy, and the manufacturers of energy-intensive products certainly have a large part to play in making this transition. But so, too, does anyone who uses electricity and gas at home, drives a car, and gets on an aeroplane.

In the UK, the energy we use in our homes and for transport is responsible for 44 per cent of the country's CO_2 emissions (see the Appendix, p 199). Reducing those emissions will involve:

- making our homes more energy efficient
- generating our own electricity and heat from renewable sources
- using alternatives to our cars, or buying the most fuel-efficient ones
- flying less or offsetting the emissions involved.

Some of those changes may in theory be achieved entirely by government through regulation, largely affecting industry. But others will require individuals to actively choose to behave differently, and to allow or encourage politicians to introduce policies to reduce our emissions rather than punishing them at the polls for trying.

Engaging with the public is critical in opening up the political space needed for government to adopt essential climate mitigation policies and reducing the public's own contribution to the problem. Without it, there is widespread agreement that climate change cannot be effectively addressed.

In the UK today, as this report shows, a large proportion of the population is failing to take action to reduce their contribution to climate change despite high levels of awareness of the problem, while parts of the population are resistant to some of the policy changes required. Developing a low-carbon economy and meeting the UK's climate change objectives depend on reversing that situation.

The UK's CO_2 emissions rose by 2.2 per cent in 2003 and 0.5 per cent in 2004 (DEFRA 2006f, Table 5), fell by just 0.1 per cent in 2005 (DEFRA 2007a), and rose again in 2006 by 1.25 per cent (DTI 2007b). If the trend persists, the Government's target to reduce CO_2 emissions by 20 per cent below 1990 levels by 2010 will be missed by a substantial margin – with just a 16 per cent reduction likely (DTI 2006a).

The sector in which government has been least effective in controlling emissions is transport. In contrast to the situation with industry, where demand for energy fell by 7.5 per cent between 1990 and 2005 (DTI 2005b), energy consumption has risen by nearly 23 per cent in the transport sector, with a growth in road traffic of 21 per cent (DfT 2005a). This has outstripped efficiency gains, leading to a rise in CO_2 emissions from transport of 13 per cent between 1990 and 2004 (DEFRA 2006d, Table 5).

Meanwhile, during that period, emissions from fuel supplied in the UK for international flights more than doubled, and these are not included in UK transport sector emissions (ibid).

Over a similar period, household demand for energy (for heat, light and powered appliances) has increased by 40 per cent, cancelling out the gains in efficiency achieved since 1990 in this sector (DTI 2006a) and contributing to a rise in household emissions of 8 per cent between 1999 and 2004 (DEFRA 2005a).

Population growth only accounts for some of the rising demand for energy. The UK population grew by 4.2 per cent between 1991 and 2004 (ONS 2005b), while energy consumption per capita rose by 7 per cent (between 1990 and 2001), as individual demand for energy grew. This demonstrates that the choices made by the public have a major influence on emissions outcomes. Yet the Government is wary of the electoral consequences of introducing some of the policy changes needed.

Over the coming decades, the challenge will become even greater as we face the need for much deeper reductions in emissions. These will require the adoption of further-reaching changes in policy and behaviour, with the acceptance, support and active participation of the public. Without that, reaching the UK's target of reducing CO_2 emissions by 60 per cent by 2050 will be impossible.

The benefits involved

The benefits extend beyond the goal of avoiding climate change. By helping the public to use energy more efficiently, and to be less reliant on fossil fuels, the Government will help meet its two other energy policy objectives: increasing energy security and reducing fuel poverty (DTI 2006a).

The more energy-efficient each household can be, and the less fossil fuels it uses, the less vulnerable will be the economy and the fuel-poor[4] to the impact of rising fossil fuel prices, and to potential threats to the security of supply from exporter countries.

This is an important consideration given that:

- oil prices have more than doubled in the last three years
- gas and coal prices have increased globally
- projected fuel prices for the long term are now much higher

---

4   'Fuel-poor' households are considered those that spend more than 10 per cent of their
    income on warming their homes and using energy for other needs, such as cooking.

- the UK has become a net gas importer, and is becoming a net oil importer
- many of the world's proven oil and gas reserves are concentrated in just a handful of countries (DTI 2006a).

An expected 35 per cent rise in energy bills since 2003 is already putting pressure on household budgets. It has also caused the number of fuel-poor households in England to double between 2003 and 2006 to 2.2 million, making it harder to meet the Government's target of eliminating the problem by 2010 (FPAG 2005).

The Government itself states that energy efficiency represents 'potentially the most cost effective way of delivering our energy policy objectives' (DTI 2006a: 29). The benefits will be seen not just by the wider economy but directly by UK citizens who, by implementing energy-efficiency measures now, could potentially save £72 billion on their energy bills by 2020 (EST 2005b). Businesses that produce or provide low-carbon technologies and services also stand to gain from the stimulation of greater demand for them from the public.

More broadly, many commentators from social and political traditions argue that enhancing personal responsibility to deal with the challenges we face individually and collectively, such as climate change, is a good in its own right (Halpern *et al* 2004).

Empowering individuals and communities to exert control and resolve problems themselves is seen as a means of improving governance, deepening democracy and rebuilding trust, moving away from a system in which decisions are always taken on their behalf. Strengthening people's sense of agency or control over their lives has also been found to increase their sense of well-being (Halpern 2005).

There is some evidence to suggest that members of the public who are concerned about the issue of climate change do not feel engaged in the societal challenge of tackling it, and feel locked into the systems and norms that fuel it (Sustainable Consumption Roundtable 2005). There is an urgent need to enable people such as these to act to reduce their contribution to the problem. And as the UK Chancellor Gordon Brown has stated, 'it is [the Government's] job to help make it easier for people to make more sustainable choices' (Brown 2007). Finding more effective ways of doing so is the subject of this report.

About this report

A great deal of research has been conducted into how public behaviours are formed and can be changed. There is a wealth of findings, from multiple disciplines, on how people think, behave and learn. Some of these are beginning to be drawn on to develop new ways of improving public health, reducing criminal behaviour and achieving sustainable development goals.

On the issue of climate change, a burst of new energy is being invested in engaging the public. Coalitions of large, member-based organisations from across civil society, and large corporations, are gearing up for major campaigns, and the media is covering the issue more than ever before. Government too is launching new communications campaigns and designing new strategies to better engage the public in action. There is a clear need to make all of these approaches as effective as possible. This report aims to help policymakers and others seeking to change public behaviour on climate change do just that.

It endeavours to do so by taking a comprehensive approach to the issue, based on:

- an extensive literature review
- interviews with experts and stakeholders
- a discourse analysis of UK communications relating to climate change.

Drawing on findings from across different disciplines (including the cognitive, behavioural and social sciences) and real-life case studies, this report suggests policies, techniques and communications approaches for promoting behaviour change so that the public's contribution to climate change can be reduced.[5]

---

5   We hope to conduct a subsequent project involving deliberative workshops with members of the public across the UK in which we would test some of the conclusions reached in this report and identify practical examples of how the findings might be applied.

1. Which behaviours need changing?

Changing the behaviour of individuals has the potential to have a signifi-cant impact on the UK's contribution to climate change. The behaviour of individuals was directly responsible for 44 per cent of the UK's carbon diox-ide (CO_2) emissions in 2004, with 56 per cent being accounted for by industry, the commercial and public sectors, and agriculture.

UK citizens are directly responsible for:

- all emissions associated with the production of electricity used in homes
- all emissions from burning gas, oil and solid fuel in homes to generate heat
- almost all (90 per cent) of the emissions from passenger car, bus and motorcycle and rail journeys (not including those associated with busi-ness use in office hours)
- just over 60 per cent of emissions from internal UK flights and from international flights departing from the UK (see the Appendix, p 199).

In 2004, UK citizens were directly responsible for some 261 million tonnes of CO_2 – almost 4.5 tonnes per person.[6]

Almost 60 per cent of an average UK citizen's contribution to CO_2 comes from using energy in the home, while individuals' transport choices (including flying) are responsible for over 40 per cent of their CO_2 emis-sions (see Figure 1).

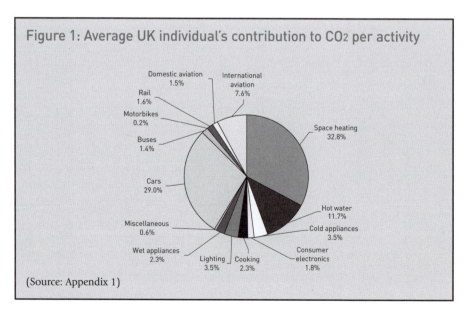

Figure 1: Average UK individual's contribution to CO_2 per activity

Domestic aviation 1.5%
International aviation 7.6%
Rail 1.6%
Motorbikes 0.2%
Buses 1.4%
Space heating 32.8%
Cars 29.0%
Hot water 11.7%
Miscellaneous 0.6%
Cold appliances 3.5%
Wet appliances 2.3%
Lighting 3.5%
Cooking 2.3%
Consumer electronics 1.8%

(Source: Appendix 1)

The specific activities that are responsible for an average UK citizen's direct annual contribution to CO_2 emissions are (in order of importance):

- space heating (32.8 per cent)
- car use (29.0 per cent)
- heating water (11.7 per cent)
- flying (9.1 per cent)
- cold appliance use (3.5 per cent)
- lighting (3.5 per cent)
- cooking (2.3 per cent)
- use of wet appliances, such as washing machines and dishwashers (2.3 per cent)
- consumer electronics use (1.8 per cent).
- bus use (1.4 per cent)
- train use (1.6 per cent)

A note of caution should be introduced about the contribution of flying. While aviation currently makes up a relatively small proportion of CO_2 emissions, the impact of CO_2 and other emissions into the atmosphere from aviation is several times more damaging for the climate than emis-

---

Box 1.1: What fuels our domestic energy needs?

- Gas supplied 70 per cent of domestic energy needs in the home in 2005. Of this total, 72 per cent was used for space heating, 26 per cent for hot water and 2 per cent for cooking. Domestic gas consumption rose by 27 per cent between 1990 and 2005 – primarily because of rising demand for heating (DTI 2006c).

- Electricity supplied 21 per cent of households' energy requirements in 2005, of which 64 per cent is used by household appliances and lighting and 30 per cent for heating and hot water. Domestic electricity consumption increased by more than 24 per cent between 1990 and 2005 – principally because of rising demand for energy from appliances and lighting (DTI 2006c).

  Of gas and electricity, electricity is the more CO_2-intensive energy source, emitting at least twice as much CO_2 per unit of delivered energy as gas in the UK. This is because such a large proportion of it is generated by burning coal (Boardman *et al* 2005).

- Petroleum and solid fuels (such as coal and wood) provide the remaining nine per cent of domestic energy needs. These are used for heating, hot water and cooking (DTI 2006c).

---

6   To convert tonnes of carbon into tonnes of CO_2, divide by their respective molecular weights: 44/12.

sions on the ground. Moreover, the growth forecast in air travel (DfT 2005a) is widely expected to make this a much greater contributor to individuals' total CO_2 emissions in future than it is today.

Individuals can reduce CO_2 emissions from each of the activities listed above by doing them less, reducing the amount of energy that is required to carry them out, or generating energy for them in ways that do not emit CO_2 emissions.

Reducing emissions from home energy use

Nearly 45 per cent of an average UK citizen's contribution to CO_2 comes from heating space and water alone. The remaining 13 per cent of home energy use comes from refrigerating, lighting, cooking, clothes washing, dishwashing, and using consumer electronics.

Consequently, changes that will do the most to reduce individuals' CO_2 emissions from these behaviours include:

- fitting insulation in cavity walls and loft spaces, and cladding on solid walls, to reduce heat escaping from the walls and roofs of people's homes
- installing a condensing boiler, to heat water using less energy
- installing microgeneration technology such as solar photovoltaic cells, solar water heaters, mini-wind turbines, or ground- or air-source heat pumps, to generate electricity and heat on site from non-CO_2-emitting sources
- switching from electricity to gas for cooking, and from coal or oil to gas or biomass for heating the home, to generate energy producing less CO_2.

In addition, switching to a 'green' electricity tariff – which involves purchasing electricity that energy companies have produced from renewable sources of energy – has the potential to reduce CO_2 emissions significantly if undertaken in sufficient numbers. Currently, most energy companies supply green electricity customers with electricity that they had already been producing from renewable sources, and hence the schemes are not displacing electricity currently generated from fossil fuels (Graham 2007).

Other changes that will reduce emissions from domestic energy-related behaviours but in a less significant way include:

- installing double-glazed or high-efficiency-glazed windows, insulating raised timber floors and insulating water boilers, to prevent heat loss
- purchasing A-rated appliances and compact fluorescent light bulbs, to ensure that electricity is consumed more efficiently
- turning down thermostats and reducing heating hours, to produce less heat

- not over-filling the kettle, not under-filling dishwashers and washing machines, switching off the lights when not in use, not leaving appliances on standby and buying fewer appliances, to consume less electricity.

Reducing emissions from transport choices

Car use is responsible for almost one third of an average UK citizen's entire contribution of CO_2. Their remaining contribution of CO_2 from transport choices comes mainly from flying. Consequently, changes in behaviour that will do most to reduce individuals' emissions from these behaviours include:

- cycling, walking and using public transport, to cut down on car use
- buying alternatively-fuelled or bi-fuelled cars and alternative fuels (such as biofuels), to power cars from lower or non-CO_2-emitting sources
- buying the most fuel-efficient car possible (such as those with smaller engines or with hybrid engines), to consume fuel more efficiently
- driving more efficiently (known as 'eco-driving') by, for example, complying with speed limits on motorways (driving at 70mph instead of 90mph reduces emissions by 25–30 per cent (personal communication from EST to authors, 2007), ensuring tyres are at the correct pressure, correct use of gears and smoother braking, to use fuel more efficiently
- taking holidays nearer to home or by train, and taking fewer but longer holidays abroad, to cut down on flying.

In addition, offsetting emissions, by investing in projects that reduce emissions by the same amount as is emitted from flying (or from other activities), has the potential to reduce CO_2 emissions significantly if offset schemes are properly accredited and activities certified to be additional to what would have happened anyway.

Less direct means of reducing individual emissions

People can also affect climate change through less direct means, such as:

- purchasing food and consumer products that have been made using less energy, and that have been transported smaller distances
- investing savings or pension contributions in climate-friendly investment funds
- clearing, rather than opposing, planning applications for wind farms
- taking part in campaigning and lobbying activities to encourage decision-makers to take action on climate change.

Each of these provides a legitimate and potentially valuable avenue of individual action. However, in most cases it is still very difficult to make accurate assessments of the significance of particular actions of this type.

In some cases, such as opposing or supporting wind farms, there are clearly problems of attribution. For other areas, such as the embedded carbon in food, data is still very limited (although studies are now under way – for example, by the Food Climate Research Network). The supermarket giant Tesco has now indicated that it aims to provide information about embedded carbon from the production, transport and consumption of all 70,000 products it stocks, but it estimates that this will take up to five years (Rigby *et al* 2007).

In addition to a lack of good data, choices do not always neatly conform to expectations. For example, eating locally grown apples out of season is not necessarily lower in embedded carbon than eating apples shipped from New Zealand if the local product has been stored in chilled warehouses for months (Garnett 2003). The science of knowing the right direction of behaviour change is still in its infancy.

For these reasons, this report will focus mainly on changes in behaviour relating to energy use in the home and in transport (including flying), whose contribution to climate change through emissions can be easily measured.

Conclusions

With individuals in the UK responsible for close to half of the country's CO_2 emissions, behaviour change should be considered an important part of the UK's efforts to meet its emission reduction targets.

An analysis of the emissions data reveals that heating of space and water in people's homes is the single largest contributor to an average UK individual's share of emissions in a given year, currently responsible for almost half the total. Consequently, efforts to reduce the loss of heat, and to increase its generation from low or zero-carbon sources, appear to deserve prioritisation.

Equally, with almost one third of an average UK individual's share of emissions originating from car use alone, increasing the use of alternatives to the car and increasing the use of lower-carbon vehicles also needs to be a priority.

While flying currently makes up just less than a tenth of an average UK individual's CO_2 emissions, its climate change potential is several times greater and its overall share is set to grow significantly. Therefore, in the absence to date of technologies to allow low- or zero-carbon flying, efforts to reduce flying and at the very least to offset emissions that arise from it appear necessary if mid- and long-term emission reduction targets are to be met.

2. What is the public doing about climate change?

We have seen which changes in behaviour are needed to mitigate climate change, but what have individuals in the UK actually been doing to date? To what extent are people changing their behaviours – whether as a result of a personal desire to mitigate climate change, or in response to policy interventions by government?

In this chapter we will look at what the public is doing so far in two areas:

- in the home
- through transport choices.

What is the public doing in the home?

Despite consistent messages from agencies such as the Energy Saving Trust (EST) over the last 15 years, UK householders have the worst record in Europe for energy efficiency, according to a recent poll (EST 2006f).

Activities related to energy efficiency, which we discuss below, include:
- installing insulation
- using energy-efficient products
- adopting energy-efficient behaviours and habits
- generating electricity from renewable sources
- switching to a green electricity tariff.

Installing insulation
There remains significant scope for households to make improvements in insulation across some, if not all, areas:

- Almost two thirds (63 per cent) of homes that could have cavity-wall insulation have not installed it (DTI 2006c)
- Almost half (48 per cent) of homes that could have loft insulation fitted at the optimum depth (4 inches) do not have it
- Almost half (45 per cent) of homes have fewer than 80 per cent of their windows double glazed.
- However, 94 per cent of homes have hot water-tank insulation.

Buying energy-efficient products
A-rated appliances
Consumers are increasingly buying the most efficient appliances available, as sales of EU energy-efficiency-labelled white goods demonstrate. In

2005/06 A-rated appliances represented 72.5 per cent of sales, and sales of all B to F-rated appliances have fallen since the introduction of the Energy Label (personal communication from EST to authors, 2006).

The introduction in 2003 of the A+ and A++ categories for cold appliances has yet to make a significant impact, but sales have been growing steadily, with up to a 4.5 per cent market share taken by A+ rated refrigerators in 2005/06 (personal communication from EST to authors, 2006).

One note of caution: it is difficult to distinguish between consumer choice motivated by efficiency standards versus minimum product quality standards. The indication is that a growing number – 58 per cent – of people claim to consider energy efficiency when making appliance purchases (EST 2004a, EST 2005a). But qualitative interactions suggest a complexity of factors, such as style, design, colour, materials, price and compatibility still take precedence (Darnton 2004a).

Hot water boilers

Until 2005, the take-up of the most efficient, condensing type of boiler was estimated at just 6–8 per cent of new boilers being purchased (EST, personal communication from SBGI to authors, 2006). Despite positive life-time savings, take-up was very low, in contrast with the widespread adoption of condensing boilers in countries such as the Netherlands. With changes to the UK Building Regulations in 2005 making condensing boilers mandatory in most situations, 89 per cent of sales are now of the condensing variety (personal communication from SBGI to authors, 2006). Nevertheless, there are still around 15 million boilers that need to be replaced – around 70 per cent of the total stock.

Energy-efficient light bulbs

Just 2.5 per cent of the approximately 250 million light bulbs sold each year in the UK are compact fluorescent lamps (CFLs) (EST 2005e). CFLs on average save 75 per cent of the electricity otherwise consumed by a standard incandescent or tungsten bulb, and last up to 12 times longer (EST 2006e).

An average house has approximately 19 light fittings suitable for CFLs (Palmer and Boardman 1998), of which 11 are medium- or high-use fittings, which are cost-effective to replace with CFLs (DEFRA 1998). EST estimates that the average home has 2.7 CFLs (based on DEFRA's Market Transformation Programme). This means that a further 8.3 CFLs could be installed cost-effectively per house – some 75 per cent of the cost-effective potential, or 86 per cent of the total potential.

If more CFLs appear to be used in homes than are actually being bought, it may be because a large number are now handed out for free under government-instigated initiatives such as the Energy Efficiency Commitment.

It has also been discovered that when a positive purchasing behaviour is adopted in relation to energy saving – especially with buying CFLs – there is a 'rebound effect'. This is where people leave lights on for longer, since they think they are using less energy (which is analogous to increased 'comfort-taking' associated with insulation measures, whereby people turn their thermostats up when they feel they have reduced energy use through other means) (DEFRA 1998). It is unknown to what extent this off-sets the gains made by the light bulbs having been replaced in the first place.

The heat-replacement effect must also be taken into account: as CFLs are used to replace standard bulbs, the heat that was generated by less efficient bulbs may be replaced by other sources, thus slightly diminishing the energy saving.

Growth in appliances

The increases in efficiency that have taken place have been unable to offset the growth in the number of appliances, and the energy consumption associated with their use in people's homes. Between 1990 and 2004, the number of appliances used by households rose by 50 per cent (DTI 2006c). Total energy consumption from appliances increased by 18.6 per cent between 1990 and 2000, and is anticipated to rise by a further 12 per cent by 2010 (EST 2006e), fuelled by greater levels of disposable income and falling manufacturing costs.

While the total energy consumed by cold appliances such as fridges and freezers has decreased by 10 per cent, between 1990 and 2004 all other product areas increased their consumption of energy. The most rapid growth was for 'brown appliances' – generally, fashionable consumer electronics – up 58 per cent.

Some new generations of products use less electricity than those they replace. For example, LCD televisions use less power than traditional cathode-ray televisions. But others actually consume more. Plasma televisions, for example, consume more than 4.5 times more energy than an average television (Boardman *et al* 2005), and sales of plasma televisions grew from 2,000 in 2001 to some 299,000 in 2005 (personal communication from EST to authors, 2006).

Ownership of telephone chargers and set-top boxes also increased by more than 1,500 per cent and 960 per cent respectively between 1990 and 2004. Some of the largest areas of growth have occurred in devices that continually consume electricity in passive stand-by mode (EST 2006e).

This trend could be exacerbated by the switch to digital TV. It is expected that there will be 50 million set-top boxes in UK homes by 2012, fuelling a predicted growth in electricity demand from consumer electronics of more than 73 per cent between 2004 and 2010, which would dwarf the energy consumption of any other sector except for heating (EST 2006e).

> ## Box 2.1: The energy cost of the growth in single households
>
> [Between 1990 and 2004 the number of households grew by 10.4 per cent, driven largely by an increase in the number of people living alone (ODPM 2006a). Declining household size has had a significant impact on energy consumption in the domestic sector, with per capita consumption increasing as household size decreases (Boardman *et al* 2005). One-person households have particularly high energy consumption. This is because they have a higher space–person ratio but a similar number of appliances to other households. This is a growing trend: in 2005 29 per cent of people lived alone (ONS 2006), and in 2026 some 72 per cent of housing growth is expected to be a result of the rise in single-occupancy living (ODPM 2006b).

Adopting energy-efficient behaviours and habits

Polling is frequently used as the basis for assessing what actions people take to reduce their impact on climate change. While self-reported behaviours provide some indication of existing awareness of solutions, and action being taken, these are unreliable and not to be fully trusted. The results of polls are subject to high levels of overstating or over-claiming by individuals – especially when people are talking about pro-environmental behaviours (Holdsworth 2003). Brook Lyndhurst/MORI (2001) estimated that people claim to recycle approximately 10 to 15 per cent more than they actually do.

The problem remains that it is difficult to assess whether people really do, for example, turn the television off at standby or fully fill their dishwasher. The inability to check people's claims has its own effect on the public response, since consumers are thought to be more likely to over-claim if they know they cannot be 'found out'.

Another problem is our inability to determine the frequency and intensity of action: whether a habitual action has been changed on a one-off, weekly or permanent basis. While people do, and rightfully, respond that they have 'turned off unnecessary lights', it may be on just one occasion, or maybe for a week. But this is not sufficient to accumulate long-term, sustained reductions in CO_2.

Although imperfect, behavioural polling may offer some, limited insight into the extent to which people are adopting small energy-saving behaviours.

Turning down thermostats

The majority of the public say they turn their heating down: 55–78 per cent of respondents claim to do so (EST 2004a, Sale Owen 2005).

Central heating is now present in 92 per cent of homes, so more rooms are heated, and there has been a rise of 1.9°C in internal domestic temperatures between 1990 and 2004 (DTI 2006c). While some homes in the UK are still not adequately heated, and require greater levels of consumption to tackle fuel poverty for health reasons, many homes do not use their heating systems appropriately.

Switching off appliances and lights
More than half (52 per cent) of people claim not to leave appliances on standby, according to one survey (EST 2005a). An exceptionally high level – over 70 per cent – claim to switch off lights or appliances when not in use and fill appliances with appropriate amounts of water (EST 2004a, Sale Owen 2005). However, Brook Lyndhurst *et al* (2003) identified that people do not turn off appliances at the wall when not in use as readily as they turn off lights (32 and 81 per cent do so respectively).

It is also likely that other behavioural trends and usage patterns have changed, such as using lower-temperature washes and greater consumption of microwave meals, but these are hard to quantify (Boardman *et al* 2005).

Overall, it is difficult to conclude what proportion of the public genuinely tries to reduce their energy consumption through small changes in behaviour. At face value, a reasonable number appear do so, and less optimistically, if they do not practise these behaviours daily they seem at least to recognise them as 'positive' and the 'right thing to do,' even if they do not yet do them routinely.

Generating electricity from renewable sources
There are currently only about 100,000 microgeneration installations in the UK (personal communication from Renewable Energy Association to authors, 2007). At best, just 0.4 per cent of UK households possessed a microgeneration system in 2006, based on the generous assumption that there is not more than one microgeneration installation per home. Of these, 95.5 per cent are solar water-heating systems installed before 2000, which only provide heat, and do not reduce demand for electricity except where they displace electric space or water heating. Ground-source heat pumps and biomass boilers make up a further 0.7 and 0.2 per cent respectively (EST 2005b).

Of the electricity-producing technologies, solar photovoltaics (solar PV) make up just 1.6 per cent of microgeneration installations, wind 0.8 per cent and hydro power 0.1 per cent. These have made no contribution to lowering demand from the national grid. Combined heat and power (CHP) technologies represent 1.2 per cent of installations, with fewer than 1000 installations UK-wide (ibid).

Box 2.2: Approving wind farms

There is another way in which the public has an impact on the deployment of renewable energy technologies: through the public consultation and approval process necessary for wind farms to gain planning permission.

Local opposition to wind farms due to visual impacts contributed to the rejection of 40 per cent of planning applications in 2004, and 33 per cent in 2005 (BWEA 2006). Hence of 54 submissions for the construction of wind farms in 2004, 21 were refused, and of 70 submissions in 2005, 23 were refused (ibid). And the number of refusals for 2005 could yet rise, as 13 applications are still pending. In 2005 itself, approvals fell to fewer than half of those proposed.

While some opposition is justified by legitimate reasons relating to location, refusal often stems from resistance by a small, highly organised local minority supported by public figures such as David Bellamy, Bernard Ingham and Michael Howard.

Officially, the number of wind farms that are granted or refused approval is not a direct reflection of local support, but of the view of the planners, based on the quality of the submissions. However, the vast majority of applications are refused on the grounds of visual impact, and while under the revised planning guidelines this should not be the sole reason for rejection, it is viewed as an easy, subjective reason to refuse planning permission. It is also the primary reason for those who do oppose wind farms to object to planning permission. While not conclusive, it does provide some indication of the localised barriers to the construction of wind farms that exist, and some idea of the effectiveness of the vocal lobby.

There are currently 113 onshore wind farms in operation, and four offshore, with an additional 24 onshore and one offshore under construction (BWEA 2006).

Switching to a green electricity tariff

Green electricity tariffs provide a means by which consumers can theoretically choose electricity generated from renewable sources. Uptake remains low, and an insignificant proportion of consumers have signed up to these tariffs.

We estimate that about 212,000 customers are supplied by 'green' electricity, representing some 0.83 per cent of the total electricity market in 2005, on the basis of broad indicative figures gathered from each of the six major electricity suppliers and the companies that offer green electricity tariffs (personal communication from E.ON, Scottish and Southern, Scottish Power and Manweb, Npower, EDF Energy, Ecotricity, Good Energy, Green

Energy and British Gas to authors, 2006). However, at present it is uncertain whether 'green' electricity tariffs are actually leading to much additional renewable capacity being created (Graham 2007).

Whereas the market for renewables used to be driven by voluntary consumers of green electricity, it is now driven by the Renewables Obligation (RO), which requires suppliers to generate 10 per cent of their electricity from renewable sources by 2010. The introduction of the RO means that the number of customers with a green electricity tariff would need to increase to more than 675,000 in order for their demand to have exceeded the level of the obligation (FoE 2004a).

Hence, paying for a green tariff could mean paying extra to help electricity companies meet their legal obligations without necessarily increasing demand for renewable electricity. Because companies can trade their Renewable Obligation certificates, theoretically they can sell renewable electricity twice – once to the consumer, and again by selling the certificates to another company.

Nevertheless, there has been a noticeable rise in the number of green electricity tariffs offered by suppliers. This may be broadly reflective of consumer demand, which is up four-fold since 2002, when there were only 50,000 green electricity customers (FoE 2004a). But equally, this is seen as a profitable area for suppliers.

What is the public doing in terms of transport choices?

Activities in this area, discussed in turn below, include: car use, including car sharing, car clubs, buying fuel-efficient cars and 'eco' driving; using public transport; cycling and walking; air travel.

Car use

Car travel accounts for over 80 per cent of the total distance travelled by individuals in the UK, and for 62.3 per cent of journeys made.

People are using their cars to travel further, and more often. There has been an 18.5 per cent increase in the number of vehicle kilometres by car and taxi since 1990, with a 5.6 per cent rise since 2000 (DfT 2005a). The average number of trips taken per person has increased by 1.1 per cent (or by seven trips) since 1990 (DfT 2006b, DfT 2005h).

Car ownership is also increasing. There were 32.6 per cent more cars on UK roads (a total of 30.7 million) in 2005 than in 1990 – equivalent to another 7.5 million more cars (SMMT 2006a). The number of people who have access to a car has increased to 74 per cent and the number of households with two or more cars rose to 30 per cent, while car occupancy decreased from 1.62 to 1.59 people per car between 1990 and 2004 (DfT 2006b, DfT 2005f).

One survey found only 14 per cent of people claimed to have tried to use their car less for short domestic journeys, or to be more fuel efficient, in the month before being surveyed (EST 2005a). Even this may be overstating the situation. The distinction between regular habitual action and a one-off token effort is critical. Qualitative research suggests that people take occasional token efforts when it suits them, but this does not translate into radical long-term changes in daily car use (Sale Owen 2005).

Box 2.3: Run to school?

The mode by which children are taken to school has been the subject of much campaigning. The school run presents multiple problems, including causing peak-hour congestion and threatening children's safety.

Now only 9 per cent of children travel to school alone – a drop of 5 per cent from the period 1992–94. This reflects the changing nature of concerns over child safety in traffic, and over non-traffic related personal security in making these trips unaccompanied (even though the 'solution' to security exacerbates problems of safety from traffic, thus creating a vicious circle).

In 2004, 41 per cent of primary school pupils were taken to school by car – a rise of 11 per cent since the period 1992–94. This correlates directly with an 11 per cent decrease in the number of children walking to school, which fell to 50 per cent (DfT 2005f).

Car sharing

Car sharing reduces the number of cars on the road and hence CO_2 emissions. People share cars informally all the time, by giving people lifts when they share a similar journey. Formal car-share schemes aim to match up people who share a similar journey pattern. Participation in informal car sharing is likely to be far greater than organised sharing (Bonsall 2002).

Many formal car-share schemes are organised by workplaces or schools, but individuals also take out membership with car-share databases. One initiative, called Liftshare, operates a national database of individuals, and of individual business and community car-share schemes that are aimed at the school run, students, people living in rural communities and work commuters. In 2006 there were more than 100,000 members registered on the scheme – a 15-fold increase since 2003 – accounting for 20 million trips (personal communication from Liftshare to authors, 2006). This figure is believed to represent 85–90 per cent of the schemes operating in the UK (excluding those run by individual companies). But the number of people registered to take part still represents only about 0.2 per cent of the UK population.

Car clubs
Car clubs are organisations that own cars and lease them out to members. Members have shared access to the pool of cars, and pay for the amount they use.

Car-club vehicles often replace old and inefficient vehicles, and are most likely to reduce car use for regular trips, and for trips for which alternative modes of transport are most readily available. The potential of car clubs is illustrated by their impact in Berlin, where a 28 per cent increase in walking or cycling and a 35 per cent rise in public transport use was seen to take place following taking membership of a car club (Cairns *et al* 2004).

In the UK, between 30 and 40 per cent of car-club members give up their cars as a direct consequence of joining, and reduce their car mileage by 60–70 per cent. However, the remaining 60–70 per cent of members do not give up their cars, using the membership either for newly acquired access to a car or to gain access to an additional household car, and thus subsequently increase or do not change their travel (Cairns *et al* 2004).

In 2005, there were 30 car clubs in the UK (excluding those organised by employers) operating in 36 towns and cities nationwide. There has been a 30-fold increase in the number of car clubs in the UK since 2000, with more than 6000 members using 325 cars (personal communication from Carplus to authors, 2006). Pilot schemes in rural areas have shown membership growth nearly doubling that of urban clubs (Cairns *et al* 2004). However, while there is growth, car clubs remain in their infancy in the UK.

Buying fuel-efficient cars
An increasing number of more fuel-efficient cars are being purchased. Vehicle Excise Duty (VED) banding, based on CO_2 emissions, shows that there is a movement towards lower CO_2 emitting vehicles, as shown in Table 2.1.

Table 2.1: Market share of cars per VED band

VED band	CO_2 emissions (g/km)	1997	2005
A	Up to 100	0.0	0.0
B	101–120	0.0	3.3
C	121–150	7.8	30.8
D	151–165	15.1	24.9
E	166–185	32.0	17.2
F	Over 185	45.1	23.8

Source: SMMT (2006b)

In terms of fuel used, there has been a considerable shift to diesel, which averages 35 per cent better fuel economy and thus emits less CO_2 per kilometre than average petrol cars. In 2004, diesel accounted for 48.9 per cent of all motor fuel consumption, though net fuel consumption still increased by 6.3 per cent from 1994 to 2004 (DfT 2005a).

There has also been a 33.6 per cent growth in small-vehicle segments that generally emit less CO_2, such as Superminis, with a 30 per cent market share.

Sales of low-carbon vehicles (LCVs) – petrol–gas and petrol–electric hybrid cars that have lower overall emissions – have also grown. The emergence of new LCVs on to the market ensured a 134 per cent growth in petrol–electric cars in 2005, of which the Toyota Prius represented 65 per cent of the market. The DVLA fuel code reports 43,255 LCVs in the UK car fleet in 2004 – a 14 per cent rise on 2003 (SMMT 2006b).

Nevertheless, total sales of LCVs remain very low. There were 4,218 registrations in 2004, accounting for just 0.2 per cent of the total car market, and in 2005 LCV sales amounted to 6,255 vehicles, representing 0.3 per cent of the market (SMMT 2006b), 92.2 per cent of which were petrol–electric vehicles. Overall, LCVs represent only 0.1 per cent of all UK cars (ibid).

Furthermore, there has been a dramatic growth in sales of cars in higher emission categories, such as multi-purpose vehicles, sales of which have risen by 236 per cent since 1997, with 4x4s up by 140 per cent and sports cars by 47 per cent. More than 8 per cent of the 2005 market would have been captured in the newly introduced band G for cars emitting over 225g/km, which still represents a far higher proportion of cars than the most fuel-efficient bands (ibid).

Interestingly, trends shifted significantly between 2005 and 2004. Rates of growth in high-emission classes are falling, as is the number of new vehicle registrations (ibid).

'Eco' driving

Driving more efficiently – especially by keeping to speed limits in motorways, using air-conditioning less, and turning off engines when stationary in traffic jams, is not a concept recognised by most motorists.

Data from average vehicle speeds from 27 motorway sites show that a majority (56 per cent) of cars exceed the 70mph speed limit on motorways (DfT 2005a), with over one third of drivers exceeding 80 miles per hour.

Using public transport

Public transport still makes up only 8 per cent of all trips made (DfT 2005f). However, since 1990 the use of public transport has increased in all forms, except in local buses outside of London, in line with heightened levels of mobility generally.

Between 1990/91 and 2004/05 the following increases took place:
● National rail travel was up by 27.6 per cent.

- Non-local bus and coach travel was up by 29.2 per cent.
- Metro travel was up by 32.2 per cent.

The rate of increase has slowed since 2000 – except in the use of national rail, which continues to climb and is the most popular public mode of travel, representing 42.8 per cent of distance travelled by public transport.

While all modes of transport are being used more, outside of London local bus use has declined, on average, by almost 12 per cent since 1990 (DfT 2005a). The national increase over the past six years is attributed to a 54 per cent increase in bus use in London in the last ten years (DfT 2005b).

Cycling and walking

Many journeys are easily and quickly undertaken by foot or bicycle. Walking still makes up 24.9 per cent of all trips made, though this is insignificant in terms of total mileage, as it only constitutes 2.8 per cent of the distance travelled per person in 2004 (DfT 2005f). Similarly, while there has been an increase in the average length that people walk per trip, from 0.6 to 0.7 miles, the number of walking trips has fallen by 60 per person per year since 1992/94 (ibid).

On average, cycling represents only 1.5 per cent of all journeys made, and the distance travelled and number of trips taken by bicycle has fallen by 6 and 20 per cent respectively (DfT 2005f).

Nevertheless, despite cycling remaining a minority activity, there are some encouraging signs in the development and use of cycling routes. The National Cycle Network is now nearly 8,500 miles long, and in 2004 was used for more than 200 million trips – a 135 per cent increase from 2000. About 37 per cent of this increase is attributable to people consciously choosing not to use a car (Sustrans 2004).

Cycling has also increased sharply within London – up by 100 per cent since 2000. This reflects two key factors: a rise in investment in cycling from £5.5 million to £26 million in 2006, and the impact of the Congestion Charge.

Air travel

When questioned in 2005, only 4–6 per cent of people said they had cut the number of flights they took (Sale Owen 2005). Far from falling, the number of passengers flying abroad from the UK has risen by about 65 per cent, and the number flying within the UK by about 70 per cent between 1994 and 2004 (DfT 2005a). Of these, some 87 per cent of trips were made for non-business reasons – mainly for holidays and visiting friends. Just over 71 per cent of passengers flying from UK airports are UK citizens, so a high proportion of responsibility falls on UK citizens flying for leisure purposes (DfT 2005f, ONS 2005a).

The emergence and growth of low-cost airlines is largely responsible for the growth in air travel by UK citizens. In 2004, 80 per cent of flights were taken to Europe, where budget airlines have the greatest reach, and the number of flights to Europe grew by 96 per cent between 1990 and 2004. Flights to North America and further afield represent smaller absolute numbers, but have been growing more rapidly (by just over 105 and 208 per cent respectively between 1990 and 2004), and represent journeys of significantly greater length (DfT 2006b).

Taking holidays closer to home
There is no evidence that people are making any attempts to reduce the distance they travel, or use less carbon-intensive modes of travel to reach their destination.

The number of people choosing to take their holidays abroad increased by 48 per cent between 1995 and 2003, while the number choosing to take holidays within the UK fell by almost 3 per cent over a similar period (StarUK 2004, ONS 2005a).

In 1990, air travel made up about 69 per cent of all trips abroad. By 2004, it had risen to represent about 79 per cent of UK residents' trips abroad. Travel by sea and through the Channel Tunnel carried about 14 and 8 per cent of UK travellers abroad respectively in 2004 (DfT 2006b), with travel by sea declining by 25 per cent since its peak in 1994, and travel through the Channel Tunnel declining by 21 per cent since its peak in 1998 (ibid).

Offsetting
Paying a voluntary donation to offset emissions from flying is even less practised than cutting back on flights. According to a poll by the Central Office of Information (2006), just 1–5 per cent of respondents said they offset their emissions from flying (DEFRA 2006a). Only one third of people even recognise the term 'carbon offsetting' (ibid).

Offsetting activity was estimated at around 240,000 tonnes of CO_2 in 2005, of which nearly 15 per cent could be attributable to individuals offsetting emissions from their flights, amounting to 34,000 tonnes (personal communication from ClimateCare and CarbonNeutral Company to authors, 2006). This amount represents approximately 0.4 per cent of the UK emissions from aviation (8.8MtCe).

Conclusions

It is very clear from the evidence on what people in the UK are currently doing that the vast majority are not taking many actions to mitigate their emissions in any significant way.

A large number of homes are still not properly insulated. While people do increasingly buy A-rated appliances, any energy gains are more than off-set by the growth in the number of appliances in the home – especially in consumer electronics. Compact fluorescent light bulbs (CFLs) still make up only a small proportion of light bulbs bought. While people say that they turn their thermostats down, the truth is that homes are kept appreciably warmer than they were 30 years ago. Investment in micro-renewables is still a tiny niche market, as is green tariff electricity.

There is a similar picture for transport choices. A large majority of UK households are heavily car-dependent. There has been a shift to the use of buses and an increase in cycling in London, but not elsewhere. Again, car clubs and car sharing remain niche choices.

The one area of positive change is that average emissions from the nation's car fleet are coming down. However, this is largely being driven by technology rather than by consumer behaviour. Sales of hybrid vehicles and biofuels remain very small. Finally, air travel is now more popular than ever, and offsetting remains a small minority practice.

3. What are the attitudes of the public towards climate change?

The behaviour of individuals in the UK is currently not climate friendly. The evidence is clear that in the home, in the shops, on the road and in the air, people are making choices that mean steadily rising emissions. In the following three chapters we examine why this is, and seek to identify the barriers to change. We start by looking at people's attitudes to climate change and the behaviours that worsen it.

Methodological issues

First a note of warning: there are significant methodological difficulties in establishing a clear public opinion from survey data and other studies. Public attitudes towards any given issue vary significantly from one person to the next, and across different surveys. Surveys use different sampling approaches and a range of questioning techniques (see Box 3.1).

Box 3.1: Positively biased?

The way in which survey questions are framed can have a major impact on results, since they effectively help shape responses. Thus two different surveys addressing the same basic issue can come up with different findings on what supposed 'public opinion' is on the issue. A question framed in a positive way, and pointing to the implications of not taking action, will often get a higher positive response.

For example, a BBC survey found that 85 per cent of respondents responded positively to the following question: 'Some people say that we need to change the way we live in order to lessen the possible impact of global warming. Would you be prepared to do so?' (BBC 2004).

However, a 2005 EST survey that posed the same basic question in a more negative way ('The government isn't doing enough to tackle climate change – so why should I?') found that only 43 per cent disagreed (EST 2005a).

Conventional appraisals of public opinion often rely heavily on quantitative surveys that use closed questions. Such polls simply show people's immediate reaction to a question and are less useful for revealing the deeper values and motivations that help drive people's long-term and habitual behaviours. Focus groups, deliberative fora and other qualitative study methods can better provide this more contextualised response, as they allow participants more time to consider questions in the light of more information.

The other factor that makes it difficult to assess public attitudes on climate change is the volatility of these attitudes over time. As a contested and rapidly evolving issue, opinion on climate change is highly responsive to events and media coverage. News agendas, global events and governmental decisions all impact on the level of priority given to the environment over time. For example, polls conducted after hurricane Katrina in September 2005 saw a 7 percentage-point jump in the number of people believing the state of the environment would 'get worse', compared to the number before the event (MORI 2006).

Thus the interpretation of surveys and studies must be treated with caution. With this caveat, we outline some broad trends and some possible indications of how these trends may be changing, drawing on both quantitative polls and qualitative studies. All reference to 'the public' refers to majority-based representational results. In most surveys, segmentation of the public is not carried out in a sufficiently consistent or widespread fashion for detailed breakdown, though some broad socio-demographic differences are noted.

Awareness and understanding of climate change

The British public has a high level of awareness of climate change (DEFRA 2006a, Sale Owen 2005, BBC 2004, Darnton 2004a). Leaman (2004b) note that demographic subgroups make very little difference in relation to people's views on climate change. Yet recognition is often based on inaccurate or uncertain understanding and confusion about what climate change really is:

'Doesn't global warming cause climate change? There's a link between the two but I'm not too sure what it is.'

Research participant (cited in Darnton 2004a: 74)

Nationally, public acceptance that climate change is occurring is nearly unanimous, with the most recent surveys showing over 90 per cent of respondents agreeing (DEFRA 2006a, Poortinga *et al* 2006, Sale Owen 2005, Darnton 2005):

'I've noticed in my job in the last 10 years (gardener) that the seasons have extended.'

Research participant (cited in Sale Owen 2005: 24)

'Our kids don't even know what snowmen are hardly.'

Research participant (cited in Sale Owen 2005: 24)

The accumulating scientific evidence that current climate change has human causes appears to be having some impact on attitudes. A 2004 survey found that only 59 per cent believed that human activity caused climate change, with 31 per cent being indifferent or not knowing (Bibbings 2004). In contrast, in the most recent polling, some 77 per cent felt climate change was a result of human behaviour, of which 58 per cent said humans were 'mainly responsible' and 19 per cent 'entirely responsible'. Only 18 per cent thought that climate change was caused by natural changes (DEFRA 2006a).

However, there still remains a notable group – comprising about 10 per cent of the population – that dismisses the anthropogenic nature of climate change and that, while accepting that climate change may be occurring, believes it is part of natural change (Rose et al 2005):

> 'I'm sceptical about it; it's one of the cycles the world goes through.'
> Research participant (cited in Sale Owen 2005: 24)

These views make the sceptical group uniquely unreceptive to calls to change their personal behaviour. Scepticism towards climate change and human contribution is most widespread among people aged over 55 (Darnton 2004a).

Environmental cynicism is also supported by a lack of knowledge, with those more poorly informed being twice as likely to be most cynical about the dangers (Park et al 2001).

Perceptions of the impacts of climate change

The way in which the public conceptualises climate change could have an impact on people's willingness to take action. People tend to show bias towards acting on issues of immediacy and locality to themselves. Trust in personal experience over any other kind of evidence has a 'localising' effect on people's understanding and perception of risk (Bickerstaff and Walker 2001, Sale Owen 2005). However, the very terms 'global warming' and 'climate change' evoke the image of a large-scale issue, remote in both time and space.

This problem was reflected in a 2004 poll for Norton and Leaman (2004), which found that only 18 per cent of people felt that climate change was a threat locally. But the situation is complex and evolving. In more recent polls, 76 to 90 per cent of people surveyed stated they believed that climate change would affect the UK (EST 2005a, Sale Owen 2005) and that there are risks to people in Britain (Poortinga et al 2006).

Darnton (2004a) suggests that the majority of the public associates extreme weather events with climate change. Recent extreme local weather events may have had an impact on the consciousness of the wider UK public. The London and Birmingham tornados, the Boscastle flooding and the 2003 and 2006 heatwaves have certainly captured media and public attention.

Weighting climate change relative to other issues

The proportion of people who believe that the risks from climate change outweigh the benefits (66 per cent) is far greater than the 10 per cent that believe the opposite (10 per cent) (Poortinga *et al* 2006). Levels of public concern about climate change also appear to be high, with 77 per cent of respondents to a Department for Transport survey (2006c) stating they were very or fairly concerned about it, with just 23 per cent feeling not very, or not at all, concerned.

However, despite this awareness of the risks, the public does not consider tackling climate change to be a more urgent priority than other issues. In a 2004 survey, climate change was put last in a list of important issues facing the UK (BBC 2004). It is still deemed important, but the issue lacks the urgency and importance of terrorism, crime, health or education:

> 'I think a lot of people do know about it, but on a day-to-day basis it's not really affecting them to such a degree where they think "Something's got to be done, and I'm going to do it"'.
>
> Research participant (cited in Sale Owen 2005: 31)

The situation remains that people still feel that the worst impact of climate change is some way off:

> 'Nothing dramatic will happen in our lifetime.'
>
> Research participant (cited in Sale Owen 2005: 27)

> 'It's going to affect our kids more than us.'
>
> Research participant (cited in Sale Owen 2005: 27)

Even when discussed in the context of the environment, people feel that local environmental issues, such as fly tipping, the need to recycle, beach pollution and industrial pollution are more important issues than climate change (Sale Owen 2005).

Some insightful questioning from Rose *et al* (2005) helps reveal the frame in which the public understands climate change. When asked 'Which of the following do you first think of when you hear about climate change?', the most popular response – at 42 per cent – replied 'the future', while just 11 per cent regarded climate change as an emergency.

Similarly, Leaman (2004b) found no change between 1999 and 2004 in people's reluctance to 'act now' on climate change.

Knowledge of the causes of and solutions to climate change

Assessments of public attitudes often conclude that knowledge of the causes of climate change is poor (Darnton 2004a, 2005). The complexity of climate change science makes it difficult to communicate and understand, and confusion with apparently similar issues is common.

In a recent survey, only some 13 per cent of respondents said explicitly that they did not know what causes climate change (DEFRA 2006a). However, perceived knowledge is not necessarily actual or accurate knowledge.

Within research relating to climate change, there has been comparatively little focus on knowledge, as opposed to attitudes. According to Darnton (2005), qualitative studies of public understanding of climate change highlight a patchy and poor understanding of causes, based on uncertainty. A lack of conviction in focus groups or individual discussions emphasises that any apparent understanding of the issue, as displayed in polls, is shallow and incomplete.

Frequently, the hole in the ozone layer or the production of CFCs is inaccurately cited as a significant cause of climate change: between 20 and 86 per cent of people have done so (BBC 2004, DEFRA 2002, Poortinga *et al* 2006, DEFRA 2006a).

Nevertheless, burning fossil fuels and CO_2 emissions are predominately recognised as the macro-cause of climate change (Bibbings 2004, DEFRA 2002, Poortinga *et al* 2006). There are some sources of such emissions that are recognised by the majority of the population and linked to climate change. But the recognition of specific causes of climate change varies over time, and between surveys – a likely result of the saliency of climate change at specific times, and the framing of the question used to obtain the opinion.

Car travel is consistently perceived to be one of the primary causes of climate change. This could be due to concern over transport issues in general, including air pollution and congestion, making these issues more prevalent in the public mind. There is also an increasing recognition that air travel harms the environment. A survey in May 2006 found 70 per cent of respondents agreeing that this was the case – up from 62 per cent in 2002 (DEFRA 2006a).

Power stations, industry, or both are also identified as other significant contributors (BBC 2004, DEFRA 2002, Bibbings 2004, Poortinga *et al* 2006, DEFRA 2006a).

However, on domestic energy use, the surveys produce contradictory evidence. Future Laboratory (2005) found that 85 per cent of respondents were unaware of the significance of domestic energy use on CO_2 emissions, while qualitative explorations by SCR (2005) also found little conscious awareness that lights, heating or appliances use fossil fuels. In contrast, in another survey that year (EST 2005a) 68 per cent of respondents claimed to be aware of the link between climate change and home energy use. These findings may reflect confusion between the attribution of emissions to the use of energy in homes and those produced through electricity generation and in industry:

'Most houses are gas and electric, not oil. Electricity is clean energy.'
Research participant (adapted from Sale Owen 2005: 44)

These findings may be important because it has been assumed that prior knowledge about the causes of climate change fosters behavioural intentions to act on those causes (O'Connor *et al* 1999). Knowledge of solutions to climate change is strongly related to knowledge of the sources of CO_2 emissions which, as we have seen, is variable, patchy and lacks conviction.

Attributing blame and responsibility

Individuals in UK households are directly responsible for nearly 44 per cent of CO_2 emissions. However, the public does not apply the 'polluter pays' principle to itself – perhaps reflecting the patchy and poor understanding of the issue discussed above. People frequently locate the responsibility for climate change and the ability to take action at the international level. Rose *et al* (2005) found that a sizeable group of respondents (48 per cent) felt that climate change was a problem of international cooperation and proportionate responsibility:

'We can all do our little bit, but when you look at the size of our little country and you compare it to America where they drive huge great cars and wagons ... they are the biggest producers of CO_2 in the world.'
Research participant (cited in Sale Owen 2005: 38)

There is a perception that size matters. Individual responsibility is not deemed important when compared with large organisations and governments (Poortinga *et al* 2006, Norton and Leaman 2004, Sale Owen 2005, BBC 2004). In a 2006 survey, UK government and industry was felt by 58 and 56 per cent of the public respectively to have a major influence on limiting climate change (DEFRA 2006a).

As a major source of emissions, industry is often blamed and looked to for delivering solutions (Sale Owen 2005, Poortinga *et al* 2006). Some 70 per cent of the public think that car manufacturers should be legally bound to make highly fuel efficient vehicles, and 82 per cent think that manufacturers of electrical goods should make appliances that use less power on standby (EST 2005).

The public does acknowledge the contribution of individual behaviour to climate change. In a recent survey, more than 70 per cent of people accepted that they personally contributed to the production of CO_2 emissions, and thus to climate change (DEFRA 2006a). But they also said they did not believe that they had a responsibility to act to reduce their contribution, and only 7 per cent felt they personally could influence it to a large extent (ibid).

Individuals see themselves as taking actions and making choices in a framework laid out by other people and global institutions. This attitude allows them to believe that any problem derived from their actions within that system is due to a fault in its design, rather than to their own actions:

> 'Why should people be made to feel guilty in the first place, they are only making use of what's been made available, why is it our fault?'
> Research participant (cited in Sale Owen 2005: 51)

People clearly look to governments to create frameworks to ensure that if they will have to act then others have to act too, to avoid the possibility of 'free riders' (mentioned further below).

Attitudes on the ability to mitigate climate change

The question of whether people feel they are able to make a difference is clearly critical. Polls on whether people feel they can have an impact on climate change through their individual actions show a complex mix of views. A majority of people feel motivated and positive, but at the same time a rising majority say they feel fearful and frustrated (DEFRA 2006a).

Recent polls indicate a feeling of inevitability about climate change, with between 54 and 60 per cent of people feeling that the UK and the world respectively are already affected by climate change (ibid). Part of this feeling of powerlessness is related to the apparent inaction of others – especially on the international stage. Some 52 per cent believe that climate change will happen regardless of what we do in Britain (Poortinga et al 2006):

> 'If America won't sign an Accord, if China won't sign no accord and the whole of the Far East won't sign no accords, so it's only the likes of us... there's absolutely nothing we can do whatsoever.'
> Research participant (cited in Sale Owen 2005: 38)

There is a wariness of 'free riders' and the need for all actors to play their part. Of those who are making an effort to protect the environment, 61 per cent do not feel that their efforts will have any impact as long as other citizens or corporations and industry do not do the same. This is also used as a reason for those who do not take environmental action to continue not to do so (Eurobarometer 2005).

People also feel disempowered unless they enabled to engage by institutions with wider powers to facilitate behaviour change (Bickerstaff et al 2006).

One result of feelings of powerlessness and inevitability is the trivialisation of the problem, with people thinking about their response simply in terms of small adaptive measures on a day-to-day basis:

'Oh yes, climate change, that's about the weather changing. I've heard about that… yeah it's an issue, you don't know what to put on in the morning.'

Research participant (cited in SCR 2005: 39)

Despite these findings, other surveys show some support for the view that even without international agreement it is worthwhile trying to tackle climate change. In 2004, 52 per cent believed that taking action without other countries was a waste of time (Norton and Leaman 2004), but recent research from EST (2005a) found that this had fallen to only 31 per cent. Similarly, in that EST survey 84 per cent of respondents agreed that they could make a difference to saving energy and help prevent climate change. Indeed, in a 2006 survey, 69 per cent of respondents said that changing their behaviour would be the most effective way of tackling climate change (Poortinga *et al* 2006).

A note of caution is necessary, however, because views change when people are asked about their willingness to alter specific behaviours. In a survey in late 2006, YouGov (2006) found that while 60 per cent of respondents said they would be willing to improve their home insulation, only a quarter said they would be willing to take fewer foreign holidays, drive less, or club together with neighbours to install a wind turbine in order to combat climate change.

Understanding public attitudes towards climate change

Many key public attitudes towards climate change should be unsurprising given the nature of the problem. Indeed, many of the issue's inherent characteristics make climate change itself a poor motivator of behaviour change (Marshall 2005). The worst impacts of a changing climate are distant in space and time, its direct causes – greenhouse gas emissions – are invisible, and we are all responsible for producing them.

This gives climate change a very different feel from other threats that have faced people in the past and that have required an immediate response. In particular, the situation is different from that of wartime, when people face a visible external enemy, and where behaviour change can be linked to powerful social drivers such as nationalism. With climate change, there is no external enemy – we are all to blame.

As a pure 'public good', much action to mitigate climate change benefits society at large, rather than benefiting the individual directly. From an economist's perspective, everyone is seeking to be a 'free rider', because it is in everyone's interest for others to take on the costs of acting, as the individual will benefit from those actions.

From a psychological point of view, climate change provides perfect conditions for the 'bystander effect' – whereby there is mass paralysis when people are confronted with a problem but do not act because they think others will, and should, do so too. The more people involved, the stronger the bystander effect, and it is strongest in societies with strong norms of conformism (Cohen 2001).

The lack of any visible public response is part of the self-justifying loop that creates the passive bystander effect. 'Surely', people reason, 'if it really is that serious, someone would be doing something.'

Other psychological reactions are also likely to be at work here. As we have seen, although many people in the UK are concerned about climate change, and even afraid of the consequences, they feel there is little or nothing they can do about it themselves.

Being confronted with such an 'uncontrollable' threat creates an internal conflict, which psychoanalytic theory (starting with Anna Freud's groundbreaking work on defence mechanisms) suggests that people will try to resolve in a number of ways (Marshall, in Bartillat and Retallack 2003). These mechanisms include:

- angrily denying the problem outright ('psychotic denial')
- seeking scapegoats ('acting out')
- indulging in deliberately wasteful behaviour ('reaction formation')
- projecting their anxiety onto some unrelated but containable problem ('displacement')
- trying to shut out all information ('suppression').

Uzzell (2000) identifies other responses, including:

- wishful thinking (where climate change can be 'solved' with very simple measures)
- religious faith
- fatalism.

Denial has been a popular response to climate change in the past, with widespread attempts to bury fears. This has included a denial that climate change is happening at all, a denial that it has anything to do with human activities, and a denial that it will have a negative or significant impact.

Increasingly, however, denial is giving way to fatalism, displacement and acting out, which fit well with a situation in which there is a diffusion of responsibility. Here people accept that climate change is happening but, as the survey data suggest, place responsibility for action with others.

At the same time, people also use these responses as justifications to defend lifestyles that they are strongly attached to, and that they perceive to be under threat. Thus very few people want to give up flying, or walk instead of driving, and if they believe that these behaviour changes would have no real effect in any case, then this becomes a rationalisation for inaction. It resolves the dissonance between their fears and their failure to change their behaviour. These effects, as reflected in the evidence reviewed here, are very powerful in the UK.

Conclusions

The evidence base for assessing public opinion is clearly very variable, and is blurred by methodological inconsistencies. In relation to some questions, the evidence appears strong. In particular, there is clear evidence that most people in the UK accept that climate change is happening, recognise the role of human activity in causing it, and express a high level of concern about it. However, in other respects a consensus is harder to discern, or appears problematic from the perspective of those seeking the adoption of climate-friendly behaviours.

Hence, it is not possible to claim that a majority of the public believes that tackling climate change is a more urgent priority than other issues. Nor is it possible to claim that most people are fully aware of how they are contributing to the problem – with many unaware of the impact of domestic energy use, or of what practical steps they can take to mitigate it. Even more importantly, it remains impossible to claim that a large majority of the public feels responsible to act or empowered to do so. The locus of responsibility is still frequently assigned to governments, industry and other countries, while far too many still say that there is little meaningful action on climate change that they can take themselves.

4. Are communications about climate change helping or hindering change?

Much of what people think about climate change, and about their own behaviour in relation to mitigating it, is influenced by how the issues are communicated to them. The way in which an issue is framed by the mass media has a significant influence on the public discourse on that issue, as the mass media often serves as the mediator of meaning – for most people it is the main source of information on social issues. With climate change, as with other issues, other actors are also important sources of information, including the government, public bodies, NGOs and companies.

Today in the UK, more stakeholders than ever before (including every type of media outlet, the Government, environmental groups and private-sector companies) are discussing, or communicating on, climate change. But what impact are these stakeholders having? Are they helping or hindering efforts to achieve behaviour change?

To help answer those questions, ippr commissioned experts in discourse analysis to analyse current UK constructions and conceptions of climate change in the public domain (Ereaut and Segnit 2006). Their analysis used some of the tools and principles of discourse analysis and semiotics, which enabled them to map structural patterns in communications and in other discussions of climate change, and to assess their implications for connecting with mass audiences.

The materials analysed came from media coverage of climate change (including 600 articles from UK newspapers and magazines, television and radio newsclips and adverts) as well as government and government-funded, NGO and corporate communications on the issue, over a period of three months from late 2005 to early 2006. Public discourse on climate change (drawn from internet chatrooms to jokes and popular language) was also examined.

A discourse in tension

The research team reached several key conclusions. First, because of the number of opposing positions and assertions, the overall impression of the discourse on climate change in the UK is confusing, contradictory and chaotic. In the words of the report: 'It is a very noisy and messy language landscape out there.' It is likely that people take away an overarching message that nobody really knows what is going to happen, or what to do.

Second, although the climate change dialogue is still very unstable and in flux, some streams emerged as sufficiently dominant or stable to capture.

In the UK today, it is possible to identify several distinct 'linguistic repertoires' – systems of language that are routinely used for making sense of climate change and our response to it. In all, ten discernible repertoires were identified, falling into three main groups:

- alarmism
- sceptical
- pragmatic.

The 'alarmism' repertoire is fundamentally pessimistic, and is in a category of its own. The two remaining groups of repertoires are optimistic. The sceptical repertoires assume that 'despite all the fuss, it'll be all right', while the pragmatic repertoires assume that 'as long as we do something, it'll all be all right'.

The alarmism repertoire

Climate change is most commonly talked about through the alarmism repertoire, as awesome, terrible, immense and beyond human control. This repertoire is seen everywhere, and is used or drawn on from across the ideological spectrum, in broadsheets and tabloids, in popular magazines and in campaign literature produced by government initiatives and environmental groups alike.

This repertoire uses an inflated language, with terms such as 'catastrophe', 'chaos' and 'havoc', and its tone is often urgent. It employs a quasi-religious register of doom, death, judgments, heaven and hell. It also uses language of acceleration, increase, intractability, irreversibility and momentum.

In emphasising the immense and awesome scale of climate change, the implication (often not explicit) is that the issue is beyond human control. Thus the repertoire presents the problem as overwhelming, and frames our situation in terms of despair, hopelessness and helplessness – which excludes the possibility of real action or agency. This repertoire is clearly disempowering, with its sub-text implying that things are so bad that we might as well give up and carry on emitting. The ultimate danger of alarmism is that it includes the implicit counsel of despair – 'The problem is just too big for us to take on.'

However, responses to this repertoire are not necessarily always despairing in the way that might be expected. The research team argued that, especially in its sensationalist, awesome and unreal forms, the accounts of destruction that climate change will bring are secretly thrilling, to the extent that they labelled this a form of 'climate porn' (Ereaut and Segnit 2006).

The sensationalism of the alarmism repertoire, and its connection with the ultimate unreality of the movies (through the use of images and ways of speaking that are familiar from horror and disaster films), also serve to create a sense of distance from the issue. It may even potentially position climate change as 'yet another apocalyptic construction' that is perhaps a figment of our cultural imaginations. All of these features serve to undermine the ability of this discourse to bring about positive action.

The alarmism repertoire often appears alongside other messages, described below. These tend to be either those that undermine the alarmist story through scepticism, humour or trivialisation (especially in the right-wing media), or those that claim that although the threat is enormous, small actions that each of us could take could save the day.

The sceptical repertoires

The underlying message of these repertoires is that, despite all the fuss about climate change, everything will be all right. Arguing either that climate change as a result of human action is simply not happening, or that we need not worry about its consequences, their underlying message is that there is no need to change behaviour. The repertoires within this group are most clearly and commonly seen in the right-wing press.

Some of these repertoires, such as the 'expert denial' and the 'rhetorical scepticism' repertoires, deny that human action is changing the climate at all – the former using a scientific mode of expression, and the latter a more ideological one. Others, such as the 'free-market protection', 'warming is good' and 'British comic nihilism' repertoires, do not deny the existence of anthropogenic global warming, but dispute that we should be worried about it.

The 'free-market protection' repertoire argues that it would be more costly to mitigate climate change than to do nothing. The 'warming is good' repertoire argues that positive effects will outweigh negative ones (especially in the UK), and is closely related to the 'British comic nihilist' repertoire. This sidesteps serious debate and treats the whole issue of climate change as a bit of a joke, by looking forward to British wine and Mediterranean-style Cornish holidays.

While currently quite marginal, this last construction of the climate change debate is characterised as quite dangerous, because it is a very British repertoire (self-mocking and contrary, dealing with adversity and threat through humour) and tends to be found among middle the classes. With an essentially sunny view of the future, it has a powerful appeal as an alternative to the fears aroused by the alarmist repertoire.

However, the most important of the sceptical optimistic repertoires identified is what has been termed the 'settlerdom' repertoire. Rather than denying climate change or its effects, this repertoire simply refuses to engage in the debate. Like the British comic nihilist repertoire, settlerdom sidesteps scientific argument, instead invoking 'common sense' on behalf of 'the sane majority' in opposition to the 'doom-mongers' to reject and mock alarmist rhetoric. It dismisses climate change as a thing so fantastic that it cannot be true.

With the settlerdom repertoire, the complexities and uncertainties involved in assessing climate change are interpreted as proof that the alarmism repertoire is contradictory and confused, and hence not worth taking seriously. However, it is more aggressive than British comic nihilism and, instead of looking forward confidently, looks back to the past, with a dislike of anything new. Settlerdom is the most stable of the sceptical repertoires: its refusal to engage makes it immune from rationalist counterargument and impervious to new information.

The pragmatic repertoires

A final set of repertoires at work within the UK climate change dialogue are pragmatic, with the underlying message that everything will be alright as long as we do something. They take climate change and its negative impact as a given, and focus instead on responses. They tend to be seen more among liberal or left-wing media, in environmental NGO and corporate communications, and in some government campaigns.

Some of these repertoires are 'techno-optimist', promoting technology as the solution. These come either from large energy companies (where the message must overcome considerable public scepticism about motivations), or from non-establishment, more independent sources. These repertoires remain marginal, as does a repertoire most associated with environmental campaigning organisations, termed the 'David and Goliath' discourse. Here, the message is that a small number of radical heroes can change the world. This repertoire tends to use imperatives and aggressive denunciations of powerful actors, branding them, for example, as 'climate criminals'.

The most significant pragmatic repertoire is the 'small actions' repertoire. Along with alarmism, it is the most dominant of all the climate repertoires, prevalent in campaign communications of organisations such as the Energy Saving Trust and the mainstream popular press. It involves asking a large number of people to do small things to counter climate change (such as turning down thermostats, not leaving televisions on standby, appropriately filling up kettles and buying efficient light bulbs). The language is one of ease, convenience and effortless agency, as well as of domesticity.

The problem with it is that it easily lapses into 'wallpaper' – the domestic, the routine, the boring and the too-easily ignored. It can be lacking in energy and may not feel compelling.

The dominant discourse

Overall, among the many discernible ways of talking about climate change, its consequences and our responses to it, two messages vie for dominance in the UK dialogue – the alarmism repertoire and the 'small actions' repertoire. These are found most widely, and are likely to be having the most important impacts on public opinion.

In a sense, alarmism, by raising people's fears and sense of powerlessness, provokes the need for a partner discourse. For a minority, this is a denial-related discourse. However, denial is becoming less of an option over time, and 'techno-optimism' as a discourse may be gaining ground.

However, the repertoire that is most commonly partnered with alarmism is 'small actions', whether at a personal or corporate level – seen, for example, in popular magazine features, with typical headlines such as '20 small things you can do to save the planet from destruction'.

It is a particularly unproductive combination. While alarmism glorifies the scale of climate change and diminishes our sense of being able to act, the personal small-actions discourse focuses only on human agency, and effectively shuts its eyes to the scale of the issue. The apocalyptic provenance of alarmism constructs a reader who is at once terrified and entertained, but effectively distanced from the problem of climate change. Meanwhile in the domestic language used by the small-actions discourse, we see a focus on the small and mundane, but no sense of the scale or urgency of the problem or of the solutions to it.

Bringing together these two repertoires without reconciling them, by juxtaposing the apocalyptic and the mundane, seems likely to feed an asymmetry in human agency with regards to climate change, and highlight the unspoken but obvious question: how can small actions really make a difference to things happening on this epic scale? What it will tend to engender is inaction.

Box 4.1: Climate change communications in the United States: lessons to learn?

In 2000, the FrameWorks Institute in the United States set up the Climate Message Project. Its aim was to develop proposals for enhancing the effectiveness of the communications of environmental groups on climate change, to increase support for preventive policy solutions. This project, which used the strategic frame approach (see Chapter 9 of this report), involved a linguistic analysis of elite discourse on climate change in media coverage, as well as of the communications of environmental groups themselves on the issue, followed by one-to-one interviews and focus groups with members of the public and a national poll.

The FrameWorks Institute found the following:

- The more people are bombarded with words or images of devastating, quasi-Biblical effects of global warming, the more likely they are to tune out, and to switch instead into 'adaptationist' mode, focusing on protecting themselves and their families, such as by buying large vehicles to secure their safety.

- Depicting global warming as being about 'scary weather' evokes the weather frame, which sets up a highly pernicious set of reactions, as weather is something we react to, is outside human control and is seen as an 'act of God'. We do not prevent or change it; instead, we prepare for it, adjust to it or move away from it.

- Focusing on the long timelines and scale of global warming further encourages people to adapt, encouraging people to think 'it won't happen in my life time' and 'there's nothing an individual can do.'

- Highly rhetorical or partisan appeals fail to persuade anyone who is not already in the environmental base that global warming matters. Using words such as 'catastrophic' has the potential to trigger a switch into rhetorical mode, in which people tend to choose between acceptance of the term or complete rejection of it, as well as risking dismissal of the messenger as an 'extremist'.

- Stressing the large scale of global warming and then telling people they can solve it through small actions like changing a light bulb evokes a disconnection that undermines credibility and encourages people to think they are being conned into adopting the ascetic lifestyles of 'extreme environmentalists'.

- Throwing the solutions in at the end of a discussion on the issue fails to signal to people that this is a problem that could be solved.

These findings were significant because the research project found that these modes of communicating represented the norm in terms of both US news coverage and of the communications of environmental groups themselves on the issue. It showed that a typical global-warming news story – outlining the scientific proof, stressing the severe consequences of inaction and urging immediate steps – was immobilising people and causing them to believe that there are no solutions.

Source: Adapted from The FrameWorks Institute 2001
The implications for a more effective approach to climate change communications are explored in Box 10.4 on p184 of this report.

Conclusions

The study of UK climate-change repertoires commissioned by ippr shows clearly how communications about climate change, within the mass media and elsewhere, actively undermine – or at least fail to support – behaviour change. The impact is visible in the attitudinal evidence presented in Chapter 3 of this report.

The widely used alarmism repertoire evokes fear and powerlessness, and almost demands an accompanying repertoire to resolve these feelings. The sceptical repertoires all carry the message that we need not make any changes to the way we live. They deny either that man-made climate change is happening at all, or that there is any real problem with its impacts. In the more appealing and populist variants, the science is simply side-stepped and people are encouraged to put their heads in the sand, or to laugh off the whole issue.

However, the most common pairing of the alarmism repertoire is with variants of the small-actions repertoire, which tells us that by taking small actions in the home or at work, we can solve the problem. This has been the repertoire used in many popular magazine features and government-funded campaigns.

The problem with this repertoire, which at least partly explains why such campaigns have not succeeded so far, is that in the end it is not compelling. The juxtaposition of the awesome scale of climate change in the alarmism repertoire with the everyday mundane responses in the small-actions repertoire implicitly raises the question of how the latter can really stop the former. The question is left unanswered, and the public is not motivated enough to act.

There are emerging signs that this problem is now being recognised in some quarters. The Energy Saving Trust, for example, has been experimenting with new campaign approaches based on the analysis presented here (see Box 10.5 in Chapter 10).

5. What are the other barriers to behaviour change?

Some of the ways in which climate change is being communicated seem likely to foster public attitudes that are unlikely to be conducive to a shift in public behaviour. The majority of people in the UK accept that climate change is happening and that it is a serious threat – indeed, many are fearful of the consequences. However, many do not feel responsible for the problem, and nor do they feel able to make a difference.

People appear to be resolving the tension between fear and powerlessness, while simultaneously defending the material comfort that behaviour change is perceived to threaten, through denial and escapism, or by looking to others – government, corporations or other countries – to solve the problem. This is easily done when the causes of climate change are so diffuse while the benefits from taking action to avoid climate change tend to be collective, rather than purely personal.

In discussions about changing their 'comfortable' lifestyles, people are also openly honest about personal laziness, greed and disinclination to change (Sale Owen 2005). Higher levels of resistance are found when it is suggested that people ought to change their lifestyle, or when they are made to feel guilty about their behaviours (ibid).

However, other, more immediate barriers – both real and perceived – are also important in preventing behaviour change, and these are explored in this chapter. These barriers can be thought of in two categories:

- **Psychosocial barriers** – including the poor image of some climate-friendly behaviours, as well as misperceptions and a simple lack of visibility of the issue.
- **Practical barriers** – including the direct financial costs and time required to search for information and adopt new behaviours. In most instances, these barriers are related to how previous and existing policies have shaped domestic energy and travel systems. For example, paybacks on microgeneration systems are low partly because the electricity system has been set up to cater for centralised rather than decentralised generation. Equally, a planning system that has encouraged out-of-town supermarkets at the expense of high-street shops increases the hassle of shopping by bicycle.

In the real world, these two types of barriers are often closely interlinked. Psychosocial barriers mean that people are uninterested in finding ways round practical barriers, while practical barriers – usually in an exaggerated and misinformed guise – become rationalisations for psychosocial barriers.

In this chapter we will look at the barriers to a number of climate-friendly actions that people could take: conserving domestic energy; installing microgeneration systems; reducing car use; buying lower-carbon cars; and flying less.

For each of these we will consider the psychosocial barriers, followed by the practical barriers.

Barriers to conserving domestic energy

Psychosocial barriers

The psychosocial barriers to domestic energy conservation include: invisibility; a poor image; misperceptions; and habits. We will look at each of these in turn.

Invisibility

Energy is invisible and taken for granted. Many people do not link the warmth and light in their homes to electricity or gas consumption (EST 2005a). Equally, people rarely think about how much energy they use from day to day. Energy use is also not always linked to emissions and climate change. More than half (52 per cent) of respondents in a recent survey saw no link between their televisions or thermostats and climate change (SCR 2005).

Many conservation measures, such as insulation, are one-off actions that become immediately invisible after installation, with no feeling of a visual addition to a home. Many people, having undertaken some energy-efficiency measures in their homes, forget which measures they have taken and do not subsequently check for reduction in fuel bills.

Energy-efficient appliances face similar problems associated with invisibility. Since appliances such as fridges, kettles, and boilers are taken for granted as long as they work, they effectively become invisible and will not be considered for replacement with a more efficient one until they cease to do their job:

> 'I couldn't care less about the one I've got and I won't do anything until it blows up.'
>
> Research participant (cited in Darnton 2004a: 11)

Current policy and the practices of utility companies on metering and feedback reinforce this barrier. Meters are hidden away in inaccessible corners, and give virtually no useful feedback on energy use by particular appliances, time of day, or system costs.

Poor image
Conserving energy is not widely perceived as 'cool'. Being energy efficient has no effect on social standing, and is not admired by peers. At best, energy efficiency is regarded as commonsense and functional, rather than pleasurable and emotionally rewarding. At worst, energy-efficient behaviours and products have actively negative connotations:

> 'I know about energy saving light bulbs and they are awful and I wouldn't even contemplate them.'
>
> Research participant (cited in Darnton 2004a: 10)

With such a poor image, energy conservation cannot compete with the more desirable drivers of behaviour in the home – especially when it might be seen as threatening these drivers. People want to feel good about their homes, which they want to be warm, comfortable, welcoming and entertaining. They aspire to appliances that are modern, convenient and easy to use, with the minimum effort. Security concerns make people want to make their homes feel busy, filled with light and sound.

These drivers make modern living very energy intensive. We now keep our homes warmer than we did in the past, pushing total energy demand for heating up by 36 per cent between 1970 and 2001 (Boardman et al 2005).

Modern lifestyles also involve a range of new consumer goods – especially electrical and electronic goods, such as computers, games consoles, DVD and CD players, microwaves, cappuccino machines and juicers – many of which did not exist 30 years ago. Hence, use of electricity by household appliances doubled between 1972 and 2002 (EST 2006e. See also Chapter 2 of this report). What is more, we are likely to see an increased demand for air-conditioning as the frequency of summer heatwaves grows with climate change. This trend is likely to continue unless there is policy intervention.

The objectives of having a warm home and owning the latest gadgets are prioritised over saving energy, as they bring little personal emotional benefit, and cost savings that are marginal for most households. For example, the two most significant measures, installing cavity-wall and loft insulation could save a household £310–380 per year (EST 2007). Ultimately, reducing energy consumption appears to bring few positive personal benefits or tangible improvements in people's quality of life for most people (Holdsworth 2003).

Misperceptions
Many people believe that they use only as much energy as is necessary. However, the definition of 'necessary' varies between individuals. Nevertheless, people often believe they cannot reduce their consumption

any further (Darnton 2004c).

Opinion Leader Research (2005a) explored the detailed aspirations and feelings associated with the home, and found that it was an area where consumers feel that they are in control and thus able to make a real difference to the environment. Nonetheless, while feeling empowered to act in this area, 51 per cent of people do not believe that they can cut down on the energy they use at home (EST 2005a).

Misperceptions also apply to monetary cost. The capital costs of many (although not all) energy-efficiency measures and appliance-efficiency premiums are actually quite low. They are a major barrier only for people in low-income groups, who tend to be more aware of energy use in any case, because costs are a much higher proportion of their disposable incomes (Darnton 2004a). However, help with the cost of energy-efficiency investments is available, with the grant offers available through the Government's Energy Efficiency Commitment, where 50 per cent of the savings have to be made in 'priority groups' (households receiving benefits and tax credits).

Despite this, a majority of consumers feel that being environmentally friendly costs too much (Darnton 2004a, EST 2005a), and that sustainable goods and services are the most expensive option (Holdsworth 2003, Holdsworth and Steadman 2005). This partly reflects the view that the energy-efficiency ratings are an indicator of quality, so that A-labelled goods will therefore be more expensive:

'Energy efficient this and that, it's always dearer.'
Research participant (cited in Holdsworth 2003: 7)

Many people have little knowledge of costs, and the few that do know have over-inflated expectations. In one study, the average perceived cost of cavity-wall insulation was £1,139 (Oxera 2005), whereas the actual cost is around £400, and some offers available from suppliers under the Energy Efficiency Commitment provide a whole-house insulation package for just £175.

There are similar misperceptions about the paybacks from energy-efficiency investments. While overestimates of capital costs loom large, future energy savings do not appear to be an important factor in a householder's decision to fit insulation or buy energy-efficient appliances (Oxera 2005). For lower-income consumers, getting by from week to week is the main concern, so all cost-benefit decisions are made in these timeframes. But even for the better off, discounting is heavy, and decisions tend to be made on a capital-cost basis, rather than on lifetime cost. People struggle to imagine that substantial capital expenditure on energy efficiency could be repaid by a future flow of savings:

'There's no point, it's a waste of effort, you're saving pennies I think.'

Research participant (cited in Darnton 2004a: 9)'

'I really don't think the amount of electricity that I use in lighting the house each year would justify the amount I'd spend on those light bulbs.'

Research participant (cited in Sale Owen 2005: 43)

This is partly because people do not trust generalised claims – for example, that energy-saving light bulbs pay for themselves. They want proof or word from a trusted source. At the same time, the combination of weak motivation and the time costs of searching for information means that few actually do.

Habit

Habit is another important barrier. Habit plays a major role in creating the sense of what is a 'normal' level of energy use in a home, affecting such activities as the use (or non-use) of thermostats, switching on and off of lights, leaving devices on standby, and setting controls on washing machines and tumble driers. Changing ingrained habits and routine ways of doing things is difficult, so this is an important if subtle barrier to behaviour change.

Practical barriers

Practical barriers to reducing domestic energy use include: hassle and inconvenience; information costs; and split incentives. We will now look at each of these in turn.

Hassle and inconvenience

The inconvenience of organising and installing energy-conservation measures is frequently cited as the most important barrier to action (Darnton 2004c).

One element of the hassle factor is the time involved in organising the action required – checking suitability, calling and vetting suppliers, obtaining quotations, arranging to be at home to let in contractors, and buying and fitting DIY installations. Many people feel enormous time pressures in their lives, and will give greater priority to family and work than to environmental considerations. This means that even if intentions are positive, installing energy-efficiency measures can easily fall off the agenda (Holdsworth 2003).

Another important aspect is the inconvenience or 'hassle factor' of having contractors in the home (HMT *et al* 2005). Fears about noise, mess, and the presence of strangers in the home are all aspects of this.

Problems of inconvenience also arise with particular technologies. For example, it is estimated that more than 50 per cent of all light fittings and shades will not fit a compact fluorescent lamp (CFL), because, for example, dimmer switches are attached (EST 2006e). CFLs are also disliked because of their slow warm up when initially switched on. These factors act as disincentives from breaking normal purchasing routines.

People are most likely to undertake a time-consuming and disruptive energy-efficiency investment at points in time where key opportunities arise, such as when moving house or replacing old boilers. For example, 63 per cent of people feel energy efficiency is important when buying or renovating their home (EST 2005a). However, these opportunities arise infrequently. Homes are bought and sold only every 15 years on average (Boardman *et al* 2005), and boilers can last up to 20 years. So, timeliness is an important factor for any intervention.

Information costs
Most householders have highly imperfect information about energy-efficiency opportunities, offers and technologies. Their ideas are often inaccurate or outdated.

While 79 per cent of people claim to know how to cut down on household gas and electricity bills, there is good evidence that most do not have a good grasp of deeper conservation measures. For example, only 16 per cent of consumers have the information that would lead them to install loft insulation (HMT *et al* 2005), and in 2003 only 21 per cent knew of energy-efficiency schemes that were in fact available across almost the whole country (Holdsworth 2003):

> 'If we were more aware and educated about what things work, a couple might stick in the head, we might think, "I'll try and do that"'.
> Research participant (cited in Sale Owen 2005: 50)

The poor understanding of energy efficiency also means that gains made in one area may be offset by inefficiency in others (SCR 2005).

There are numerous sources of information on energy efficiency, including those from trusted sources, such as national and local government and independent groups. But fewer than 3 per cent of consumers proactively seek advice on energy efficiency (EST 2005a).

Why is it that people are not better informed? One clear reason is the lack of interest in energy consumption and conservation (SCR 2005). However, another is the time it takes to become well informed, and to gain confidence that the information found is trustworthy. The multiplicity of information sources potentially makes it harder to feel confident that one is well informed.

The time it takes to find trustworthy suppliers and contractors is also a major problem. In general, consumers are suspicious of builders, plumbers and other contractors, fearing poor standards of work and being 'conned' in areas in which they have minimal knowledge. Consumers also distrust advice from suppliers and installers of boilers, insulation and other measures – especially when capital costs are slightly higher than less efficient alternatives:

> 'It is falling into the same marketing situation as double glazing and insurance. You wouldn't trust any of them.'
>
> Research participant (cited in EST 2005d: 30)

In focus groups conducted by Bonsall *et al* (2006), consumers expressed a belief that in a commercial environment, suppliers will try to win market share through a myriad of special offers, and will often try to trap consumers into paying more by making things complex, adding restrictions and using 'small print'.

Consumers even have low levels of trust in information on energy efficiency being offered by suppliers through the Energy Efficiency Commitment, feeling that there must be a 'catch', as suppliers could not genuinely want to help consumers save money without making profit. Lack of trust in installers appears to impact on insulation take-up, more than offsetting the attraction of a 75 per cent price discount (HMT *et al* 2005).

Again, the time costs of finding out about the reliability of claims by suppliers and installers simply deter people from proceeding. While consumers express great concern over accreditation, in one study only 8 per cent were aware about existing accreditation schemes (Oxera 2005).

Split incentives
A final structural barrier to energy efficiency exists in the sector with the poorest energy ratings – private rented housing (EHCS 2006). The landlord–tenant relationship creates a 'split incentive', in which the landlords, who would face the upfront costs of capital investments, do not benefit from reduced bills, while tenants, who could benefit, may only be in the accommodation for a short period and so have no long-term incentive to pay capital costs.

At the same time, there is no rental premium associated with good energy performance in a home sufficient to drive the rental market in the direction of energy-efficient homes. For new homes, a similar dynamic exists between developers and buyers.

Overall, many of these barriers reinforce one another. The perception that capital investments are high and paybacks low, combined with a mistrust of installers, makes the hassle and risk of undertaking energy-efficiency measures very unattractive. As Paul Ekins (2003) suggests:

> 'The barriers may be institutional or infrastructural, related to social norms or expectations, derive from existing habits, lifestyles or pref-

erences, or reflect shortages of time or money, or other priorities. A single barrier of any of these kinds may be enough to prevent a public policy from having its desired effect and, if the policy includes a sanction for not changing behaviour, may generate political opposition so that it cannot be implemented.'

Barriers to installing microgeneration systems

Psychosocial barriers
The psychosocial barriers to installing microgeneration devices include image and lack of familiarity, which we discuss below.

Image
In the public mind, micro-technologies have an eccentric, 'eco-warrior' image. SCR (2005) found that among mainstream householders, microgeneration was perceived to be relevant only to those who had made a lifestyle decision to 'go green', and that it was not a part of a 'normal' lifestyle:

> 'Oh that kind of stuff that is for people who live in the countryside... who want an alternative lifestyle... not for city people. It's for those who want to get in touch with nature... you know they are probably hippies, the sort of people who would educate their children at home.'
>
> Research participant (cited in SCR 2005: 39)

Lack of familiarity
Microgeneration is still unfamiliar. Although there are a few exceptions, technologies such as micro-wind turbines and solar panels are not widely visible. People question why they are not being used, fearing that they are costly, ineffective and unproven:

> 'You never see a new house with these sorts of things on. Why aren't more people doing it? Is that because they don't work or are too expensive?'
>
> Research participant (cited in EST 2005d: 29)

The recent decisions by mainstream retailers Currys and B&Q to sell micro-renewable technologies such as solar photovoltaics, solar thermal panels and micro-wind turbines, and by some leading political figures to install them in their homes, may start to erode some of these barriers. However, it is still too early to assess the impact of these developments.

Practical barriers
The practical barriers to installing microgeneration systems include: capital

costs; information costs; and planning permission. We now look at each of these in turn.

Capital costs

Probably the principal barrier to installing microgeneration is cost (SCR 2005, EST 2005b, London Assembly 2005). Unlike the situation with energy conservation technologies, where it is perceptions that are the problem, the capital costs of microgeneration genuinely are high.

These are still emerging technologies, not yet benefiting from the economies of scale that come with mass production. While costs will come down in the future, people currently considering microgeneration are paying a premium as early purchasers of the technologies. In a survey by the London Assembly (2005), 45 per cent of respondents who expressed interest in solar water-heating systems cited overall cost, payback period or other financial issues as reasons why they had not had a system installed.

> '£7,000 is a lot of money if you do not see the return. And if you are going to stick your neck out you should get help from the government.'
> Research participant (cited in EST 2005d: 28)

Of course, some such help is available, and grants (along with some decrease in the cost of microgeneration technologies over the last five years) have increased the number of installations – for example, in photovoltaics, and increasingly in micro-wind. However, even under the new grants programme, demand has far outstripped supply, with the monthly grant rounds becoming over-subscribed within a few hours of opening. The level of grant funding is closely correlated with the annual number of installations, suggesting that capital outlay is still a major barrier to further uptake (see Chapter 7 of this report).

High capital costs mean long payback periods (see Box 5.1), and this is another dimension of the problem. In focus groups, respondents were very surprised to learn that paybacks from investing in solar panels may take decades, and felt that this was totally unacceptable:

> 'Payback in 20 to 40 years! Excuse me! Someone has got their figures wrong somewhere.'
> Research participant (cited in Brook Lyndhurst *et al* 2003: 25)

Long payback periods arise not only from high capital costs, but also because the energy system is aligned to centralised generation, with fiscal arrangements supporting this. Few electricity companies offer a reward for exported electricity that matches the price they charge, and householders – unlike power companies – cannot obtain capital allowances on their

Box 5.1: Micro-renewables: cost-effectiveness and payback periods

The cost-effectiveness of micro-renewables is clearly a major barrier to their uptake. However, before exploring this issue further it is important to make a note of caution on the figures.

The payback periods of micro-renewable technologies are dependent on many factors, including the type of technology, location, aspect and building characteristics. With all micro-renewables that produce electricity, a significant proportion of the power generated will be exported to the grid (although most meters are not set up to deal with exports). However, currently there is no guarantee of an income from such exported power (although this may change as a result of the Climate Change and Sustainable Energy Act 2006).

The calculations below do not include any such income. Similarly, Renewables Obligation Certificates (ROCs) are also omitted from the calculation, due to current difficulties in accessing these figures, as are costs relating to obtaining planning permission, and operation and maintenance costs. The figures used are generally sourced from EST, to limit commercial bias, and use an average electricity cost for March 2006.

Solar photovoltaics

An average domestic solar photovoltaic (PV) system would have a capacity of 1.5–2KWp (kilowatt peak) of electricity, or half the annual electricity demand of one home. Solar PV can cost between £4,500 and £9,000 per KWp (EST 2006c), although a typical 2KWp system would be in the region of about £12,000–£14,000 (British Photovoltaic Association 2006).

Each KWp of capacity would provide about 750 KWh (kilowatt-hour) per year, although this will depend on location, aspect and weather conditions (ibid). Given an indicative electricity import price of 10p per KWh, each KWp of capacity would save £75 each year, or £150 per year from a typical 2KWp system.

Grant funding through the Low Carbon Buildings Programme has provided a maximum £3,000 per KWp installed, up to a maximum of £15,000, subject to an overall 50 per cent limit of the installed cost. Payback in this particular case would be in the region of 45 to 60 years if full grant funding of 50 per cent were awarded. This is in the same range as other recent calculations of payback period for solar PV (for example, Watson *et al* 2006).

Without government subsidy, payback through reduced bills would take some 90 to 120 years. A system should last for more than 30 years with minimal maintenance (British Photovoltaic Association 2006), although payback on the capital investment cannot currently be obtained through reduced bills. Obviously, payback times would be reduced if householders were given a sufficient reward for exported power, as is the case in Germany and other EU countries.

Small-scale wind generators

A typical roof-mounted wind turbine will have a capacity of 1–1.5KWp, but the optimum size for a domestic wind turbine would be 1.5–3KWp. Systems up to 1kW cost around £1,500, whereas larger systems in the region of 1.5kW to 6kW would cost £4,000–£18,000, and would have a lifetime of about 20 years (EST 2006c). A good wind site will produce an average output of 30 per cent of the rated capacity of the turbine, thus, in theory, a well-placed 1KWp turbine would produce about 2,628KWh per year (EST 2006c). If this were to displace imported electricity costing 10p per KWh, this would save some £262.80 per year and would take about six years to pay for itself.

However, in practice, high wind speeds are not reached all year round, and this, together with eddies commonly found in urban areas, means that more detailed modelling of micro-wind generation produces lower output figures. For example, a recent study by Imperial College, the University of Sussex and the University of Southampton shows a 1.5KW turbine producing 590–1,680KWh/yr depending on site (Watson *et al* 2006). This would provide savings of £50–140 a year, with payback periods of between 10 and 30 years.

Costs and paybacks have the potential to change significantly on a case-by-case basis. Obtaining ROCs, exporting electricity, and replacing existing appliances with microgeneration (such as replacing roofing slate with solar photovoltaic slates) could significantly improve payback times.

microgeneration investments. These factors have a significant impact on payback periods (Watson *et al* 2006).

With many microgeneration technologies being fixed investments, and with over half of UK households moving home every ten years or less (DCLG 2006a), such long paybacks deter many people. Mass market appeal would require a much shorter payback.

For homeowners, one mitigating factor to set against high capital costs and long paybacks is the possibility of an increased price if the home is sold, above and beyond any expectation of the economic returns from the technologies. However, although there is some anecdotal support for this 'green' asset price premium – the company Solar Century gives one example of a £10,000 price premium for a house with PV – as yet, there is no evidence base to assess it on.

Thus in the present market, the costs involved with microgeneration technologies mean that they will be taken up only by more affluent members of the UK public with strong environmental motivations.

Information costs

As microgeneration technologies are relatively new, it can be difficult and time consuming for the public to locate accurate information on their performance and characteristics. Not surprisingly, lack of awareness and misperceptions are commonplace.

Most people are not even aware that it is possible to provide heat or power to their homes from microgeneration technologies rather than via the national grid. Among those who have some knowledge, solar technologies have the highest awareness scores, followed by micro-wind – but overall, home energy generation is not seen as a viable consumer choice (EST 2005d). The potential benefits of decentralised power have little resonance among the public.

Meanwhile, people have minimal understanding of the technologies and their ability to function in the UK's volatile weather patterns (SCR 2005). For example, most people think that solar PV panels will only generate electricity in bright sunlight, while in fact solar PV panels do function with cloud cover (Brook Lyndhurst 2004).

'Don't think we get enough sun do we?'

Research participant (cited in Barker 2003: 13)

Similarly, there are misconceptions about the need for a large roof, or a particular orientation (SCR 2005), and many people have doubts about the efficacy of wind turbines, partly fuelled by incorrect or exaggerated claims by anti-wind farm campaigners that have been given prominence in the media.

In addition, some people believe that if a micro-wind turbine powered their home, this would involve having a large, obtrusive turbine in their back garden requiring a large amount of space and creating a lot of noise (Brook Lyndhurst *et al* 2003). Generally, understanding of the difference between micro and large-scale wind power is very poor.

More and better information can have an impact on behaviour. Of those surveyed for a London Assembly study, 27 per cent said they were more likely to install a system having heard a summary of the costs and benefits (London Assembly 2005). But there is a lack of detailed and practical yet non-technical information on microgeneration from independent trustworthy sources, and this remains a barrier. In the same London study, 53 per cent of people who were interested in installing solar hot-water systems said they did not have access to enough information.

Finally, just as with the energy-efficiency industry, the public is mistrustful of suppliers and installers of microgeneration. Although there are over 275 microgeneration installers – with the majority offering solar products (EST 2005b) – this is an emerging sector that still lacks industry standards and accreditation schemes. Investigating the reliability of these firms is a time-consuming job that only the most committed consumer is likely to undertake.

Thus capital costs – both real and perceived – and the informational costs of overcoming doubts about the capacities of the technologies remain the primary structural barriers to more people installing microgeneration technologies.

Planning permission

Another potential barrier to the implementation of microgeneration technologies that may change following the 2006 Energy Review is the inconsistency in how different local authorities handle planning applications to install these technologies. Those authorities that still require applications introduce further obstacles, including cost, time and general inconvenience. In London, nearly 5 per cent of those who had wanted solar hot-water systems did not go ahead because of the requirements of, or complications with planning permission (London Assembly 2005).

Barriers to reducing car use

The barriers to reducing car use are a complex and often indistinguishable mix of the practical and psychosocial. To a large extent, the UK's physical infrastructure has been designed for, and enabled by, the car – and our social structures have also been enabled by this mode of transport, making society more car dependent. There are a range of motives for car use at the individual level, identified by Bamberg (1999) as including: perceived personal benefits; lower perceived costs in relation to alternatives; perceived situational restrictions; pressure to social norms; role identity; affective evaluation; and habit.

It is increasingly likely that social and emotional factors are more important than cognitive evaluations of time and cost (Anable 2005). However, there is little evidence about the relative importance of these barriers (Anable *et al* 2006).

Psychosocial barriers

The psychosocial barriers to reducing car use include issues relating to: denial and displacement; status and identity; and misperceptions about cost. We now look at each of these in turn.

Denial and displacement

People's attachment to the car can lead them to hold views that at some level they know to be contradictory, or even false. For example, the strength of people's attachment to their cars persists in the face of awareness that car use is highly damaging to the environment (OLR 2005a). This attachment can also lead people to subconsciously block the known links between emissions and car use (Darnton 2004a, 2004c). It can also partly explain why many people state that public transport alternatives are too costly, inconvenient or uncomfortable while admitting that public transport is good in their area (Holdsworth 2003).

People's attachment to the car can also be seen in their tendency to claim that others are responsible for solutions to problems arising from car use. There is a general acceptance that 'everyone' is to blame for congestion, but the most popular solution to improve public transport relies on 'other people' changing their behaviour (Grayling *et al* 2006). People would be keen for others to switch to public transport, thus improving the road conditions for themselves – although this would, of course, be impossible in the aggregate (Green and Stone 2004).

Status and identity

If people are so attached to cars, it is partly because they represent much more than just a mode of transport. The car is a status symbol and an expression of personal identity. Hence, a significant proportion of the public aspires to have increasingly more prestigious, top-of-the-range models (Grayling *et al* 2006). This behaviour stems from strong and widespread norms that material wealth brings happiness and respect. Owning one of these 'desirable' vehicles is one way of displaying and feeling such gains:

> 'I don't think... people worry about the fuel in their car. What they want to know is the status symbol of the kind of car that they drive.'
> Research participant (cited in Holdsworth 2003: 14)

The same factors are attached to driving at high speeds, which is often closely bound up with owning a powerful car.

In contrast, public transport (especially buses) is regarded as a lower-status mode of travel, with a dislike of bus travel linked to a feeling that it undermines self-image (Stradling *et al* 2004). Margaret Thatcher famously stated that anyone over 30 using a bus was a failure, and public transport is often stereotyped as a 'poor person's alternative' and thus not aspirational. These perceptions run counter to the reality of travelling by bus. There have been rising levels of passenger satisfaction with bus services – particularly in London. The principal barrier to increased bus use is the poor perception of the service by those who do not use, or infrequently use, buses (DfT 2006a).

The same status issues apply to cycling. DFT (2002b) found that 13 per cent of people thought their friends would laugh at them if they cycled more, while 10 per cent thought their friends would feel sorry for them if they walked more.

Many people see cycling as eccentric, heroic, socially unacceptable or of limited relevance (TfL 2004b). A national study by the Transport Research Laboratory indicates that 38 per cent of non-cyclists worry that friends would laugh at them for cycling (TRL 2001), compared to only 4 per cent of existing cyclists. Concern that others see cycling as an activity associated with a low social status is a deterrent that will only be overcome by the development of a critical mass.

Misperceptions of cost

Drivers seldom estimate, or consider, the cost of making an individual car journey. The current structure of costs for car use does not incentivise behaviour change. Upfront expenses such as road tax and insurance are quickly forgotten once paid, and are thus not taken into account when comparing the day-to-day running costs of cars with alternative modes. On average, motorists underestimate car costs by half of the actual costs – especially when it comes to the servicing and repairs (Lane 2005), and over-estimate the costs of public transport:

> 'And the prices. You may as well have a taxi as go on public transport.'
>
> Research participant (cited in Bibbings 2004b: 63)

Paying for public transport is often seen as an additional expense, rather than an alternative to car use, which helps to explain this exaggeration of cost (Holdsworth 2003):

> 'We don't go on the buses – as an extra expense.'
>
> Research participant (cited in Holdsworth 2003: 7)

Paying for services as they are consumed tends to draw attention to cost – a so-called 'announcement effect' (DfT 2006d). Thus frequency of payment also has a significant influence on the perception of cost. Costs of car use are therefore perceived as lower than those of public transport. This situation is not helped by the fact that between 1980 and 2004 the cost of rail and bus fares rose by almost 40 per cent in real terms, while the overall cost of motoring fell by 10 per cent (DfT 2006b).

However, efforts to increase the cost of driving through fiscal measures such as road pricing would generate a great deal of resentment:

> '[Road tax] would just make us moan.'
>
> Research participant (cited in OLR 2005b: 34)

Indeed, people tend to believe that they have paid for the right to drive already, through existing taxes. Imposing additional costs, such as congestion charging, would interfere with this right that they feel they already 'own' and make them feel they are paying twice (Green and Stone 2004). This is believed to be simply unfair.

Practical barriers

The practical barriers to reducing car use include convenience and habit. We now look at each of these.

Convenience

Nine out of ten motorists say they would find it very difficult to adjust their lifestyles to being without a car, and admit to using their car every single day (RAC 2006). When challenged, a common reaction is for people to claim that they have no alternative to car use (EST 2005a). Even for short journeys, the majority of people do not consider the bus to be a viable alternative (National Centre for Social Research 2006):

> 'It is impossible to manage without a car.'
>
> Research participant (cited in Bibbings 2004b: 63)

There is a widespread perception that the way that society is arranged makes a reduction in car use impossible. Within the spatial and temporal arrangements for work, shopping and leisure that have evolved over the last 50 years, people's attachment to cars is, from an individual point of view, rational. Cars are often more convenient, even in the face of rising congestion and pollution (Bird and Vigor 2006). No other mode is currently able to offer the degree of personal space, comfort, control, safety, or convenience that the car provides. People also like the spontaneity and independence that car use appears to give – to the extent that they do not consider the sustainability implications at all (OLR 2005b).

While the convenience of an alternative depends on the distance, the task to be undertaken, and the weather, a car is suitable for almost all conditions, and thus is a convenient choice every time:

> 'I wouldn't care if someone said we'd pay you £20 not to use your car on one day a week, it's not practical. You're not going to stand at a bus stop with a two year old.'
>
> Research participant (cited in Sale Owen 2005: 14).

Inconvenient bus routes, scheduling, concerns over safety and discomfort have all been given as reasons for people disliking bus services (Anderson and Stradling 2004, Stradling *et al* 2004). Some even actively resent public transport, which they see as expensive, slow and unsafe at night, and as taking up space and financial resources (Sale Owen 2005).

When it comes to cycling, people frequently cite concerns about safety and the ability to carry heavy items as key reasons for not cycling more. In a report by the Scottish Executive (2006) the most frequently mentioned barriers were poor weather (36 per cent) and a cluster of concerns about cars and safety. Research carried out by the Department for

Transport (2002b) found that 85 per cent of women and 61 per cent of men agreed that cycling on busy roads frightened them. Transport for London (2004b) identified seven barriers to cycling in London, including danger, weather and a poor environment for cycling.

Non-cyclists also cite the effort involved as a further discouraging factor. Not being fit enough, being too lazy, the journey taking too long, having to cycle too far, and getting hot and sweaty on the way to work are cited as reasons for not wishing to cycle (TfL 2004b). The lack of shower and parking facilities at work and train operators' restrictions on carrying bicycles also help to reinforce the perception that cycling is not a socially acceptable mode of transport (ibid).

Some of these concerns have a rational basis. However, as with over-negative perceptions of public transport, they tend to be exaggerated, and users have a very different perspective from that of non-users. While 65 per cent of non-cyclists believe that there are too many obstacles preventing them from cycling, this view is shared by only 24 per cent of existing cyclists (Transport Research Laboratory 2001). There is also a widespread, inaccurate, perception of the time taken to use alternative means of travel to the car, and a lack of information about public transport (personal communication from Sustrans to authors, 2005).

Here, as with domestic energy efficiency and microgeneration, the time required to access accurate information acts as a barrier to behaviour change.

Habit

Research from BMRB Social Research (Green and Stone 2004) showed that habit is an important determinant in people's travel behaviour. As we shall see in Chapter 7, habits that are repeated frequently, that have strong associated rewards, and that are rewarded quickly after completion are the most difficult to break. This suggests that changing behaviour for regular journeys, such as the daily commute to work, will be difficult – especially as there are strong rewards, such as the convenience and comfort associated with current behaviour.

Barriers to buying lower-carbon cars

As well as using cars less, people also have the choice to lower their emissions from car use, by driving cars that produce fewer emissions. The RAC Foundation (2006) believes that attitudes to car purchasing are changing. The Society of Motor Manufacturers and Traders (SMMT 2006a) recently revealed that today, safety (23 per cent) and fuel economy (18 per cent) take precedence over top performance (4 per cent) in guiding choice of car, once motorists have decided on a budget (52 per cent). However, it also found that despite fuel economy taking greater precedence, low emissions are considered by very few (3 per cent). Motivation appears to be driven mainly by finance, especially in light of fuel costs, rather than environmental issues.

Psychosocial barriers
The psychosocial barriers to buying lower-carbon cars include: belief that government is responsible; poor image; and misconceptions about products available. We now look at each of these in turn.

Belief that government is responsible
More than two thirds of people (70 per cent) believe that the Government is responsible for the uptake of vehicles that are more environmentally friendly. Just 17 per cent put this responsibility in the hands of the driver (Environmental Transport Association 2006).

Poor image
Inasmuch as consumers are now faced with a choice, low-carbon vehicles can be perceived as ugly or unattractive. There is little research that explores the explicit link between the aesthetic appeal of a vehicle and whether it is low carbon or highly efficient. Some consumers – especially young, low-income consumers who aspire to own a car – see sustainable cars as an embarrassment. 'Green' (including lower-carbon) cars do not have the emotional attraction of traditional, especially 'high-performance' models:

> 'Smaller cars are ****** horrible. Most of them anyway.'
> Research participant (cited in Holdsworth 2003: 14)

Misconceptions about products available
Drivers have negative misconceptions about the safety, range, performance and reliability of new fuels or technologies, and these make people wary. Many even see 'miles per gallon' as an aspect of car design that can only be achieved by compromising performance and safety (Lane 2005):

> 'You can put petrol in your car and it takes you miles. An electronic car – you have to keep on plugging it in… you'd have people pushing them all over the place.'
> Research participant (cited in Holdsworth 2003: 7)

Practical barriers
The practical barriers to buying lower-carbon cars include: the higher price tag; information costs; and infrastructural barriers. We will look at each of

these in turn.

Higher price tag
As with microgeneration, the fact that some lower-carbon cars use emerging technologies means that they currently do involve a premium.

For example, the Toyota Prius hybrid costs between £3,765 and £5,385 more than the Toyota Corolla 1.4 or Avensis 1.8 – its petrol-fuelled equivalents. This price difference on vehicles costing under £18,000 acts as a significant barrier to all but the strongly environmentally motivated. Savings in fuel consumption and road tax would pay back the cost difference only after between seven and 12 years (ippr's own calculations, based on What Car list prices and AA Motoring Trust figures for the cost of unleaded petrol in May 2006). In a recent survey, just over one third of respondents (34 per cent) said they would rule out buying a hybrid simply because they believed they were too expensive (Environmental Transport Association 2006).

However, while cost stands as a real barrier to the purchase of hybrids, it should not prevent people from purchasing the most fuel-efficient vehicles within a car class. Usually, lower-emission vehicles not only cost less to run but also tend to have a cheaper showroom price tag, due to smaller engine sizes.

Information costs
While demand for driving choices is driven heavily by psychosocial and price factors, another barrier may be the low level of detailed knowledge and understanding of lower-carbon choices (Lane 2005). For example, research conducted on behalf of Honda found that more than 40 per cent of the 1,200 people questioned did not realise that hybrid cars use both petrol and electric power (Environmental Transport Association 2006).

As with other areas of behaviour, because the lower-carbon route is still a niche choice, it can take time for potential consumers to access accurate information that they feel they can trust. And while for some the idea of hybrids and biofuels are novel and exciting, others can be put off by detailed technical accounts (Darnton 2004a).

Similar information-related problems apply to eco-driving. Most people are unaware that driving fast increases emissions per mile, or that switching off engines while stationary can save significant emissions.

Infrastructural barriers
Low-carbon choices in driving are also seriously limited by a lack of infrastructure. Car makers such as Saab are now offering models that can run on a mix of 85 per cent bioethanol to 15 per cent petrol, but there are only a handful of fuelling stations, in East Anglia and the West Country, that can offer this mix. While this may change in future, it currently represents a major barrier to the uptake of biofuelled cars.

Barriers to flying less

As with car use, despite an awareness of the environmental impact of flying, curtailing plane usage is fiercely resisted. In a recent survey, 78 per cent of respondents were in favour of continued access to unrestricted air travel (DEFRA 2006a), as long as environmental damage was limited. However, it is not clear that individuals accept the need to pay the costs of this limitation. In a 2005 study, Mintel found that 72 per cent surveyed were even unwilling to pay a surcharge to offset the carbon emissions of their flights (Robbins and Bowes 2005). Even among the 'environmentally keen,' 80 per cent remain resistant to cutting back on the number of flights they take (Sale Owen 2005).

Psychosocial barriers

The psychosocial barriers to flying less include: sense of entitlement; lifestyle image; and increase in desire for long-haul travel. We now look at each of these in turn.

Sense of entitlement

Air travel – especially for holidays – has come to be seen as an inextricable element of the widening of prosperity and improvement in quality of life in modern Britain (OLR 2005a) – and this is even more the case than with access to cars. Once seen as a luxury for the privileged few, now everyone feels entitled to fly, and people are even less willing to cut down on this 'entitlement' than they are on driving (Bibbings 2004b).

Lifestyle image

Research for the Sustainable Consumption Roundtable showed that many people aspire to flying abroad. In a 2006 ONS omnibus survey for DfT, the desire to travel abroad was the most frequently cited reason for planning to fly in the coming year (DfT 2006a). In contrast, the UK is not seen as an attractive holiday destination, which is one reason why cutting back on flying is not an attractive option (OLR 2005a).

Increase in desire for long-haul travel

There has also been a limited shift in the destinations to which people choose to go on holiday, with more people favouring long-haul holidays than was the case in the past. Increased competition, combined with the rise of low-cost carriers, has played an important role in this – together with a change in attitudes, with tourists becoming more adventurous and seeking more exotic destinations (Graham 2006). However, the majority (76 per cent) of international trips made by UK residents are still to European destinations.

Practical barriers

The practical barriers to flying less include: cost; and time and convenience. We now look at each of these.

The view that flying is the norm for travel abroad – and, increasingly, within the UK – has been underpinned in recent years by a number of trends, including the deregulation of aviation, the rise of low-cost airlines and the growth in regional airports.

Cost

The shift since 1990 away from sea and tunnel travel towards flying (Graham 2006) can be partly attributed to travellers becoming wealthier and therefore better able to purchase air tickets. But it is also due to the fact that the real costs of flying have fallen dramatically over the past 30 years. Average fares paid by UK residents at 2004 prices for long-haul leisure flights have fallen from over £1,000 in 1970 to just over £200 in 2004 (Cairns and Newson 2006, DfT 2006b). Short-haul flights have fallen in real terms too, although less dramatically. The average short-haul fare is now under £50.

The impact of the low-cost, no-frills carriers can be seen in the changes in the number of passengers carried. Domestic no-frills carriers increased passenger numbers by 550 per cent between 1998 and 2002, while other domestic carriers lost 11 per cent. Similarly, passenger numbers of international no-frills carriers were up by 292 per cent over the same period (Cairns and Newson 2006).

Time and convenience

Flying has the obvious advantage of being faster than ground-based travel in reaching almost all overseas destinations (the exceptions being trips from London to Paris or Brussels), and in some cases within the UK too. Airlines are also seen as providing a better service than train services (OLR 2005a). The fact that more of the smaller regional airports in the UK now offer direct flights to Europe has further increased the convenience of air travel.

The convenience of flying matters partly because people are taking shorter, more frequent holidays. The average length of international holiday trips from the UK decreased from 12.0 days in 1991 to 10.2 days in 2003 (Graham 2006). This is attributed partly to the rise of short breaks overseas – itself a trend made possible by increased air travel. And while the length of trips has decreased, the total number made has increased (Cairns and Newson 2006).

Conclusions

When we look at most of the behavioural changes needed to combat climate change, we can find a host of factors that explain why people cling firmly to old, climate-unfriendly behaviours and steer clear of new, climate-friendly ones.

Overarching barriers appear to be the lack of a strong sense of responsibility and agency for tackling the problem, as well as a generalised attachment to a comfortable material lifestyle that behaviour change is perceived to threaten. Beyond that, for each specific change in behaviour sought, an interlinked combination of barriers can be found in a range of practical concerns, as well as a number of psychological and social factors that prevent change.

With energy use in the home, the status quo is perpetuated by the invisibility of energy, people's overriding desire for warm, bright, convenient and entertaining homes, and engrained day-to-day habits. Conservation measures, on the other hand, fail to bring any personal benefit in terms of social status and emotional fulfilment, and only marginal cost savings for most households. They also suffer from a poor image, and are perceived to involve high upfront capital costs (with lifetime costs and discounts typically ignored), taking time to organise, and being inconvenient to install – particularly as suppliers are not trusted.

Microgeneration technologies suffer from being largely unfamiliar and still not widely visible. They have an eccentric image, fuelled by misconceptions about their effectiveness, and it can be time consuming to find out about and install them. But the single most significant barrier to their uptake is the high capital cost and unacceptably long payback periods involved – particularly for solar PV. These factors are compounded by the difficulty in getting a fair reward for exported electricity and Renewable Obligation certificates.

When it comes to car use, the status quo is perpetuated by people's strong attachment to the car, based on its perceived superiority over alternatives in terms of its ability to provide high social status, independence, convenience, comfort and safety, and at a lower perceived cost than alternative modes of transport. Meanwhile, lower-carbon cars suffer from image problems, misconceptions about performance, higher upfront cost than equivalents and, in some cases, a lack of infrastructure.

Finally, cutting back on flying is strongly resisted because people want to travel abroad rather than holiday in the UK. The tendency is increasingly to travel further than before, for more exotic holidays, and to take shorter but more frequent trips. In those circumstances, flying is the most convenient form of travel, given its speed, and has become much more affordable as the cost has fallen significantly.

6. Has the traditional approach to behaviour change worked?

The following five chapters explore how government and others can most effectively intervene to remove the barriers that people face in changing their behaviours. In this first chapter, we look at the traditional approach to effecting change, and consider how far this has worked.

Historically, governments worldwide have relied heavily on the law and its enforcement to impose obligations on citizens and thereby influence public behaviour. For example, over the past 40 years this has been seen in legislation to ban drink driving, to make the wearing of seat belts compulsory, to apply anti-social behaviour orders, and to ban smoking in public places.

But in many areas of public policy, compulsion has either not been effective on its own (this is true for the areas of public policy mentioned in the previous chapter), or has not been an option at all. Regulation is appropriate and possible only for certain types of behaviour – for example, it would be impractical to regulate small, repeated behaviours like turning lights off or thermostats down. And often, the degree of interference with people's private lives and choices that compulsion would involve has not been deemed acceptable, democratically justifiable or politically viable – particularly in an era in which the sovereignty of consumer choice prevails.

In such circumstances, governments have tended to rely on two other sets of approaches to influence behaviour: the provision of information and the use of fiscal instruments. The deployment of these tools has often been more politically expedient, but historically this has also been justified on the basis of the 'rational choice' model of human behaviour. This model assumes that humans behave so as to rationally maximise their welfare by making systematic use of the information available to them and assessing the choices before them in terms of costs and benefits.

Until recently, policymakers traditionally relied on two approaches derived from the 'rational choice' school of thought:

- *The 'information in, action out' approach* This holds that providing information to increase knowledge will lead to greater awareness and concern, in a linear fashion, creating attitudes that, in turn, will lead to desired behaviours.
- *The 'price signals' approach* This holds that behaviours would change by applying price signals through taxation or subsidies that would increase the costs associated with behaviours that they seek to discourage, and make the behaviours they seek to encourage appear more beneficial.

Here, we briefly assess the success of these approaches.

The 'information in, action out' approach

This linear model of behaviour change has been the basis of pro-environmental strategies and communications campaigns for governments and non-governmental organisations since the early 1970s. However, it is now widely accepted that it does not work. Fostering awareness of a problem, the threat it represents, its causes and what can be done about it will not necessarily lead to action being taken.

There can be no more obvious example than the provision of information about unhealthy behaviours. Even if people know that some of these behaviours will actually kill them, some will continue to engage in them anyway. This 'awareness–action gap' applies to many pro-environmental behaviours too. Research reveals that in most cases, increases in knowledge and awareness alone have not led to pro-environmental behaviour change (Kollmuss and Agyeman 2002).

The UK Government's 'Are you doing your bit?' energy-saving campaign launched in 1998 is a well-known example of a campaign that is thought to have raised awareness of environmental problems and solutions but caused no discernible change in behaviour. In fact, research into the causes of behaviour change that has taken place has found that only a small fraction can be directly attributed to environmental knowledge and awareness (ibid).

Empirical evidence suggests that attitudes and behaviour can change without any assimilation of new knowledge or persuasive messages, and that learning and behaviour change can occur without any change in attitudes (Greenwald 1968, Petty and Cacioppo 1981). Indeed, in some cases it is a change in behaviour that precedes and is responsible for a change in attitudes, because we sometimes infer what our attitudes are by observing our own behaviour (Bem 1972). For example, if a person starts recycling not because they think it is a good thing, but because the facilities to do so have been made conveniently available, they may then start thinking of themselves to some extent as being environmentally-minded (Jackson 2005).

The danger of relying on changing attitudes as a means of changing behaviour is also highlighted by research suggesting that when people's actions and attitudes clash, a desire for consistency can lead them to change their attitudes rather than their behaviour (Halpern *et al* 2004). The incentive to re-adjust long-term goals rather than change a lifetime's habit may be particularly strong when the rewards from the behaviour are high (Jackson 2005).

Supplying people with more and more information about why they should be replacing one behaviour with another in their already crowded lives will not make the changes any easier to actually make. It may widen their 'circle of concern', but will not widen their 'circle of influence.' It could even be counterproductive, as it may undermine people's strong desire to feel in control of their lives, and to resist feeling helpless (Jackson 2005).

This is confirmed by research showing that increasing levels of information about environmental problems makes people feel more concerned but also more helpless. When people feel their actions will not make any difference, they are less likely to change their behaviour (ibid).

Box 6.1: Information overload – how we defend ourselves from bad news

When we are exposed to a painful or fearful experience, our primary emotional reaction may be distress. Our secondary reaction may be a series of psychological responses aimed at relieving us of these negative feelings. These psychological responses are defence mechanisms, and may include denial, distancing, apathy and delegation. Each of these responses may prevent us from altering our behaviour in the necessary way:

- **Denial** is the refusal to accept reality. When we are in denial, we filter out incoming information to fit our own preferred version of reality. Exposure to more information about a problem simply increases our urge to avoid it.

- **Rational distancing** happens when we are aware of a problem but have stopped feeling any emotions about it. The more we are exposed to bad news, the more likely we are to develop this self-protecting mechanism.

- **Apathy and resignation** take place when we feel strong emotions about a problem but feel helpless to do anything to change the situation. We ignore any information about the problem, and focus on other things instead.

- **Delegation** is the refusal to accept personal responsibility for a problem ,which we blame on others instead.

Source: Adapted from Kollmuss and Agyeman (2002)

As we have seen, providing information is not an answer in itself. However, this is not to say that a basic knowledge about environmental problems, and the behaviours that cause and solve them, is not an important factor in acting pro-environmentally. The theory of planned behaviour contends that a person's attitudes about a given behaviour will influence their behavioural intentions, along with a number of other factors. According to this theory, behavioural intention is the key determinant of our actions (Ajzen and Fishbein 1980).

There is also evidence to suggest that people with high levels of environmental awareness are more willing to accept policies aiming to encourage pro-environmental behaviour, such as higher fuel taxes (Diekmann and Franzen 1996). However, the balance of evidence suggests that providing information to raise awareness and foster appropriate attitudes is not sufficient for action to be taken.

The 'price signals' approach

The second strategy that stems from the 'rational choice' school of thought involves applying price signals through taxation or subsidies. It has been more effective in changing behaviours than the 'information in, action out' model.

We know that people are sometimes self-interested, and are swayed by cost. Hence, evidence suggests that when the costs of pro-environmental behaviour are comparatively low – not just economically, but also in terms of time and effort – and if pro-environmental attitudes have been forged, then behaviours have been changed (Diekmann and Preisendörfer 1992).

This approach has clearly worked in some cases, such as the switch from leaded petrol, when unleaded petrol was made the cheapest form of fuel. It also worked to achieve a 90 per cent reduction in the consumption of plastic bags in Ireland, when the government introduced a 'PlasTax' of 15 cents per bag at the point of sale, accompanied by a comprehensive information campaign (Collins et al 2003).

Another successful example is the London congestion charge, introduced in 2003 and involving a charge for each vehicle travelling into the designated congestion zone during peak hours on a weekday (£5 at the time of introduction and now £8). Together with a 22 per cent increase in bus services and lower bus fares, the charge has brought about a 30 per cent reduction in congestion in the zone, a net reduction in car traffic of about 35 per cent, and a 19 per cent reduction in CO_2 emissions from within the zone (TfL 2006, Holdsworth 2005).

In another success story, the Belgian city of Hasselt provided free bus transport (together with an upgraded and more frequent service, with new buses and more routes). This initiative contributed to an 870 per cent increase in bus use in three years, and a decrease in car use (Holdsworth 2005).

As we have seen, the use of the 'price signals' approach has had some success. But sending the right price signal is rarely sufficient on its own. Indeed, it is well known that many pro-environmental behaviours that offer net financial benefits to individual consumers are still not being adopted on a sufficiently wide scale – and this includes many behaviours related to energy efficiency. In 2002, the Cabinet Office Performance and Innovation Unit reported that:

> 'There is a broad consensus... that energy users do not seek to optimise the economic efficiency with which they use energy (PIU 2002). Interestingly, even though retail prices for gas and electricity have risen steadily over the last two years by 50 per cent and 35 per cent respectively, gas and electricity use has hardly changed, with only a small dip at the end of 2006.'
>
> (DTI 2007a)

Box 6.2: The psychology of fiscal interventions

Financial incentives and disincentives work in slightly different ways:

- **Disincentives** – in the form of taxes and charges – work through our aversion to loss, and can help overcome habit and inertia, to stop existing behaviours (see Chapter 8 of this report). Using them to stop environmentally damaging behaviour can be made more politically acceptable by making sure the revenue raised is spent on expanding the provision of alternatives.

- **Incentives** – in the form of subsidies or rebates – can be used to create new behaviour, by supporting weak social norms and motivations to act in the desired way. In particular, tax rebates are often popular to an extent that is out of proportion to the amount on offer. This has been demonstrated in the case of council tax rebates aimed at encouraging people to insulate their homes (see Chapter 7 of this report).

Where the success of this model of behaviour change has been limited, this has been because the assumptions on which it is based have been flawed. The model assumes, for example, that people act out of individual self-interest, and that 'rational' behavioural outcomes result from conscious deliberation. In fact, neither of these assumptions are necessarily the case (Jackson 2005). We know, for instance, that people often behave out of habit, without thinking much about it at all. We also know that people often behave for social, cultural and moral reasons, not just self-interested financial ones (as we shall explore in Chapter 8).

Conclusions

The 'rational choice' model of human behaviour has dominated public policy for decades. When compulsion has not been an option, governments have tended to pursue two main approaches: the 'information in, action out' approach and the 'price signals' approach. Of these, the latter has generally been more successful than the former.

While having knowledge about environmental problems is one factor in acting pro-environmentally, on their own, greater knowledge and pro-environmental attitudes have frequently failed to translate into pro-environmental behaviour change. Indeed, in some cases, it has been a change in behaviour that has caused a change in attitudes. In others, supplying people with information may have been counterproductive when it has not been accompanied with measures to empower people to act.

Using taxes and subsidies to discourage behaviours and encourage others has a better track record, as people's decisions are sometimes swayed by cost. But once again, evidence suggests that price signals alone are rarely sufficient. Indeed, in some cases, factors other than rational calculations about cost are more influential in determining behaviours, in which case price signals may fail to stimulate behaviour change at all.

The limitations of rational choice as a sole basis for public policy are clear from the poor performance of some of the interventions designed on that basis. But it is also increasingly recognised within the cognitive sciences that individual rationality is profoundly embedded in, and dependent on, the social environment (Hurley 2006, Halpern *et al* 2004) and psychological make-up of the individual concerned, as we shall see in Chapter 8. Rational choice is just a starting point.

7. What is the Government doing to change climate-related behaviours?

Until very recently, the UK Government has mostly used variations of the traditional methods described in Chapter 6 of this report to try to influence behaviour to mitigate climate change. Interventions have largely fallen into five main categories (Boardman *et al* 2005).

- **Regulating consumption** – mostly by applying regulations upstream, so that in some cases the outcome is not dependent on consumer choice at all – as, for example, with building regulations.
- **Promoting leadership** – working with industry on voluntary agreements that are aimed at providing leadership that enables behaviour change. The Government has also indicated that it will act to provide leadership by example, through procurement and other activities.
- **Setting incentives and disincentives** – Using taxes, subsidies and other measures as a way of influencing the price of using goods and services that reduce or increase emissions – for example, on the one hand effectively subsidising insulation and low-energy light bulbs while on the other placing higher taxes on cars emitting more carbon per mile driven.
- **Providing information** – Legislating to communicate information on emissions so that it is visible to the public, or to encourage others to provide that information.
- **Contributing to campaigns** – Supporting public campaigns that encourage behaviour change – including those delivered through the Energy Saving Trust, the Carbon Trust and most recently by regional and local organisations.

This chapter reviews and assesses the interventions that the Government has made to try to change behaviour in relation to domestic energy and transport. Climate-change communications often span a number of areas of behaviour change, and so these are assessed separately at the end of the chapter. In some cases, government action is only recent, so a full assessment is not always possible.

This chapter summarises the Government's inputs in the following areas: domestic energy; microgeneration; road transport; and aviation. It considers each of these themes within the five categories of activity listed above.

Domestic energy

The Government's aim is for all homes to have achieved their cost-effective energy efficiency potential by 2020 (HMT 2007). Its interventions to reduce levels of domestic energy use can be summarised as follows:

Regulating consumption

The two main areas in which regulation plays a role in changing behaviour on domestic energy are in relation to building regulations and product standards.

Building regulations

The impact on behaviour of the Government's building regulations is most immediately visible in what developers and the mass house-builders do, but it feeds through into the choices of individual home buyers.

Minimum standards of energy performance in all new buildings and for retro-fitted construction work are set under Part L of the building regulations. There are required standards in both commercial and domestic buildings.

The most recent 2005 revisions in Part L of the building regulations will save an additional 0.8MtCe from the 2002 standards that came into effect in April 2006 (DEFRA 2004a). But they were weaker than initially proposed, delivering a 20 per cent improvement in energy efficiency on the 2002 standards rather than the draft proposals of 25 per cent. These standards fall behind the best in Europe, and have missed opportunities to improve whole-house efficiency when extensions are undertaken (House of Lords 2005).

The 2005 building regulations also have implications for boilers and lighting. When a gas-fired boiler needs to be replaced, the 2005 building regulations require it to be in the Seasonal Efficiency Database of Boilers in the United Kingdom (SEDBUK) band A or B (ODPM 2004a), which in most cases effectively means a condensing boiler.[7] This has had a dramatic effect on the sales of condensing boilers, and it is estimated that by 2020 approximately 75 per cent of existing boilers will have been replaced with this type (EST 2006e).

However, in the short term the Building Regulations may act as a disincentive to replacement. If people did want to replace an ageing boiler, rather than try to prolong its life with maintenance or part replacement, the regulations would oblige them to buy a condensing boiler, which is significantly more costly than conventional boilers. In addition, some five million homes have systems that do not facilitate easy replacement with a condensing boiler.

---

7   Typically, a condensing boiler will save 37 per cent of the energy used by a conventional type. Sales of condensing boilers stabilised at about 85 per cent of the UK market in January 2006 (personal communication from SBGI to authors, 2006).

Building regulations also effectively require a minimum number of compact fluorescent light bulbs (CFLs) to be installed in newly built homes. However, there is evidence to suggest that because CFLs are often supplied in stick form (which is compatible with only a small number of lampshades), many people replace them shortly after moving in (EST 2006e). There are other CFLs that are compatible with a wider range of lampshade fittings, but these are more expensive.

Compliance with the regulations has been an issue in the past (Shorrock and Utley 2004), though measures announced in the 2006 Energy Review aim to simplify and clarify the regulations while strengthening enforcement (DTI 2006a).

Building regulations will be reviewed every five years from 2010, setting a long-term direction for the building industry. The Code for Sustainable Homes (see below) will form the basis for the next wave of improvements. The Government hopes this will enable it to reach the goal of making all new homes 'zero-carbon' by 2016, meeting the highest code standard for energy efficiency (HMT 2006b).

Product standards
Beyond the fabric of homes, minimum product standards for appliances discourage the production of the worst-performing products and practices by manufacturers, suppliers and end users. Statutory minimum standards for traded goods need to be agreed at EU level, since the establishment of the common market. This means that raising product standards depends very much on the influence and commitment of the UK and other member states at the EU level.

Product standards are highly cost effective and beneficial to customers, and there is no evidence of costs being passed onto consumers if manufacturers are given time (two to five years) to absorb them into product development cycles (HMT *et al* 2005). Minimum standards, combined with the EU energy label in 1999, improved the energy efficiency of cold appliances in the UK by 15 per cent, and were accompanied by a 14 per cent drop in prices (Boardman *et al* 2005).

In contrast, the consumer electronics sector has trended towards higher-consuming devices, such as plasma televisions, as a result of unregulated growth in this area (Boardman et al 2005). Goods that sit on standby currently contribute about 1.2 MtCe (House of Lords 2005), and in 2004 were responsible for 8 per cent of all residential electricity (DTI 2006a). Consumption from standby is between 5 and 30W, even though a figure of about 0.1W is technically achievable (SDC 2006b).

The EU Directive on Eco-design of Energy-Using Products (EuP) establishes a framework for 'eco-design' standards that will include energy consumption from standby. The directive does not introduce directly binding requirements for specific products, but it does define conditions and criteria for eco-design, and allows them to be improved over time.

The UK adopted the EU EuP legislation in 2005, and it is set to become law in the UK in 2007. Recently, proposals were brought forward to set standards for 14 products, including consumer electronics, lighting, heating and white goods, and could potentially avoid 1.3MtCe by 2010 (DTI 2006a). The directive sets out a three-year plan to ensure that new products are designed to minimise energy consumption.

Historically, agreement on minimum product standards has been on an ad-hoc basis, and has seen positive as well as negative impacts. Despite the EuP Directive, the EU appears to be moving away from minimum standards towards voluntary agreements (see below). These are weaker, and take longer to impact on the market (Boardman *et al* 2005). Nonetheless, collective product policy has had a very positive effect in transforming the efficiency of markets.

It is also worth noting that the Energy Efficiency Commitment (EEC) has helped to promote best practice by providing consumers with products of the best environmental standards (see below). The experience that users have of those products will strongly influence them to continue to buy such appliances.

Some 6.6 million appliances were supplied through the Energy Efficiency Commitment in 2002/05, with £600 million invested (Lees 2006), helping to increase the sales of A-rated wet and cold appliances from around 10 to 60 and 80 per cent of their markets respectively (Ofgem 2005b). Recognising the potential savings possible through consumer electronics, the distribution of 0.5 million set-top boxes has been incorporated into the EEC II illustrative mix (DEFRA 2004b).

In addition, the first phase of the Energy Efficiency Commitment saw the distribution of 39.7 million CFLs (Ofgem 2005a) – some six times the number sold by retailers (although concern has been expressed about the number handed out when compared to the number actually replacing conventional light bulbs, and some fear that grant-dependency may distort the market (Boardman *et al* 2005, EST 2005e)).

Promoting leadership
The two main areas in which government initiatives to promote leadership play a role in changing behaviour on domestic energy are in relation to voluntary manufacturer agreements and the Government's proposed carbon-neutral office estate.

Voluntary manufacturer agreements
In transforming markets, minimum product standards are complemented by voluntary manufacturer agreements. These have not been particularly

effective at bringing about rapid or large changes in product efficiency, and gains have been more than offset by rebound effects – both in the trend for larger products, and in the constant growth in new kinds of products. However, they can play a role in paving the way for the implementation of higher regulatory standards in the future (as with condensing boilers).

Between 1996 and 2000 the standby consumption in colour televisions was reduced by about 50 per cent, as a result of using voluntary agreements, but the inconsistency of policy in this area meant this saving was wiped out by growth in other areas, such as plasma televisions (Boardman *et al* 2005). The EU voluntary agreement on digital television services will save around 0.2 MtCe by 2010 compared with the 'do nothing' scenario (HMT *et al* 2005). Voluntary agreements can help deliver some emissions reductions, but these types of arrangements generally do not have the security to deliver in short time frames.

The carbon-neutral office estate

The Government also intends to lead by example on the use of energy in buildings by pledging to ensure all of its own buildings are carbon-neutral by 2012 (DTI 2006a). This will include the use of offsetting, although it also involves setting targets for energy-efficiency and procurement standards. It is predicted that this initiative will reduce energy use by 10 per cent through behavioural change, and by a further 5 per cent by using more efficient products and services.

Setting incentives and disincentives

The main government incentive and disincentive initiatives that play a role in changing behaviour on domestic energy are: the Energy Efficiency Commitment; the Warm Front and Decent Homes initiatives; reduced VAT; stamp-duty exclusion.

The Energy Efficiency Commitment

The most significant government intervention on domestic energy use is the Energy Efficiency Commitment (EEC). The EEC places an obligation on energy suppliers to deliver energy savings in homes by encouraging customers to install insulation, energy-efficient appliances, lighting and heating – partly by offering subsidised products. The costs of the EEC – around £400 million per year – are funded by a levy on all energy bills.

The target for Phase I of the EEC (2002–05) was 62TWh of energy savings. This figure was exceeded by 35 per cent, and the excess carried over to contribute towards Phase II. The target for Phase II (2005–08) has been doubled to 130TWh – equivalent to savings of about 0.6 MtC annually by 2010. The Government has committed to a Phase III (2008–2011), and has a proposed target in the range 0.9–1.2 MtC (DEFRA 2006e).

Under Phase I of the EEC, around 10 million households benefited from free and subsidised energy-efficiency improvements, saving customers around £350 million. Insulation – especially cavity-wall insulation – is the most favoured way of delivering savings, with 56 per cent of savings being delivered through providing insulation to homes. Across all groups, Phase I delivered the following (Lees 2006):

- more than 790,000 new cavity-wall installations
- more than 1.1 million new top-up DIY loft-insulation installations
- nearly 200,000 hot water-tank insulation measures
- nearly 24,000 solid-wall insulation measures.

However, despite these achievements, the Energy Efficiency Commitment has so far failed to have sufficient impact to stop the underlying upward trend in domestic energy consumption – especially of electricity – of about 1 per cent per year. A key reason for this is that the approach taken by suppliers under the EEC does little to encourage consumers to consider their energy demand and purchasing behaviour, and its effect on the environment (Ofgem 2005a).

As a result, proposals for a different approach to the EEC tend to relate to ways of making the issue of energy use more visible to householders. Smart metering, which allows suppliers to be credited for making real-time information on energy use available to householders, is one example (see below).

Another approach is linking energy to more visible issues, such as council tax. Innovative rebate schemes, pioneered by British Gas under its Energy Efficiency Commitment obligation, have been successful at stimulating interest in the whole-house energy-efficiency package that is on offer. Households are offered a one-off £100 rebate on their council tax bill in exchange for taking advantage of the subsidised £175 package.

Following its successful pilot in Braintree District Council, in Essex, the scheme has been extended to a further 16 local authorities, with a reach of some 880,000 residents nationwide. However, while a further 40 councils are in discussions with British Gas, the current extension still only reaches about 3 per cent of the UK's 10.3 million domestic cavity walls that are still to be filled.

The most significant proposal has been to transform the Energy Efficiency Commitment from a commitment to encourage householders to undertake efficiency measures into a commitment to encourage them to actually reduce energy use (Grayling *et al* 2005) – a measure that would now be possible under the 2006 Climate Change and Sustainable Energy Act.

In such a scheme, suppliers would be given energy-reduction targets to achieve across their consumer base. Rather than putting their effort into selling gas and electricity to consumers, this would (in theory at least) give suppliers a real incentive to sell them efficient 'energy services' – in other words, the same warmth, light and power, but with a lower overall use of energy – instead. This idea has been taken up by the 2006 Energy Review, and will be put out to consultation, but is not being considered as a policy option before 2011.

The Warm Front and Decent Homes initiatives

The Government has also had some influence on domestic energy, through two schemes aimed at fuel poverty and social housing: Warm Front and Decent Homes. Although not aimed at climate behaviour per se, these schemes have improved levels of insulation significantly. Under Warm Front, around 200,000 homes a year – some 1.5 million in total – have received assistance at a cost of about £200 million a year (DTI 2006a). An additional £300 million has been available to UK fuel-poverty programmes between 2005 and 2008, taking the total to £800 million.

However, as with the Energy Efficiency Commitment, these schemes have been designed to minimise the involvement of the public, rather than working through behaviour change. In the case of Decent Homes, better insulation is delivered entirely through social housing providers, with tenants not involved at all.

Reduced VAT

Another price incentive available to householders is reduced VAT. Since April 2000, all insulation and draught stripping that people pay to have fitted has been subject to VAT at a rate of 5 per cent, reduced from the standard 17.5 per cent – the maximum reduction possible under EU agreements. Not only does this lower the absolute cost of undertaking improvements in insulation; it also enables consumers to feel as if they are avoiding tax, which is an attractive concept. However, DIY installations and purchases remain subject to the full 17.5 per cent VAT rate.

Stamp-duty exemption

In the most recent incentive for improved energy efficiency in new homes, confirmed by the Government in its 2007 Budget, a stamp-duty exemption will be introduced in 2007 for new 'zero-carbon' homes costing up to £500,000, and a discount of £15,000 will be offered for all zero-carbon homes costing over £500,000. These measures, which will be time limited for five years until September 2012, are designed to incentivise demand for 'zero-carbon' homes among homebuyers (HMT 2007).

Overall, a problem for the 'incentives' approach is that, as noted in Chapter 6, price is not a very effective driver of behaviour change in domestic energy.

Over the past two years, domestic gas prices have risen by around 50 per cent and electricity prices by 35 per cent (DTI 2006e). These increases have been primarily driven by the global oil market, but also by the introduction of the EU Emissions Trading Scheme (EU ETS) and by the Renewables Obligation, where generators have passed on the costs of carbon and renewable electricity to consumers.

These price rises are equivalent to a rather large carbon tax. However, while these changes have impacted significantly on the fuel poor, there has been virtually no impact on domestic energy use overall. For the large majority of households, energy costs remain invisible.

Providing information

The main government-backed information-providing initiatives that have played a role in changing behaviour on domestic energy are: the work of the Energy Saving Trust, including its Energy Efficiency Advice Centres and Sustainable Energy Network; information on energy bills; 'smart' meters; Home Information Packs; the Code for Sustainable Homes; and product labelling.

The Energy Saving Trust

The main government-funded agency providing advice to householders about energy efficiency is the Energy Saving Trust. Set up in the wake of the 1992 UN Conference on Environment and Development in Rio de Janeiro, the EST encourages energy saving in the domestic and transport sectors, as well as championing the use of small-scale renewables.

Energy Efficiency Advice Centres

Much of the EST's work with the public has been carried out through a network of 46 Energy Efficiency Advice Centres across the UK, often run in partnership with local authorities or social enterprises. EEACs are the primary source of official information on energy saving for the public, and have been advising around 750,000 people annually, with a budget of almost £8 million in 2004/05.

However, despite EST campaigns (see below), the low priority that most people give to energy efficiency means that the EEAC network has not been seen as succeeding in catalysing a step change in behaviour. Resources are spread thin, advice is only available over the phone or online, and energy audits have to be carried out by householders themselves.

The Sustainable Energy Network

A recent reorganisation of the EEAC has seen the creation of a Sustainable Energy Network (SEN) at regional level, in addition to the existing EEAC network, to try to be more strategic and to coordinate government information and campaigning efforts in each area. The EST is currently piloting three Sustainable Energy Centres that replace some of the EEACs. The idea is to target local campaign activity to the specific needs of the area, partnering with local organisations and the supply chain to achieve carbon savings through energy efficiency, microgeneration and sustainable transport.

The pilot takes a coordinating role in bringing together key players, and targeting national initiatives to greatest effect locally. The network provides sustainable energy and transport advice and support, acting as a focal point for national awareness-raising and information campaigns. Results from early SEN trials have been positive, and show a 65 per cent increase in carbon savings since the previous period, when only the EEAC network was in operation (EST 2006b).

This improvement has been attributed to the more focused approach of the network, involving better identification and targeting through promotional and partnership activities of the key carbon-saving opportunities in their areas (personal communication from Energy Saving Trust to authors, 2007).

Certainly, local EEACs are now experiencing a greater demand for information on domestic energy-saving measures as the visibility of climate change as an issue in the media has dramatically increased (personal communication from Lucy Padfield, Energy Manager, London Borough of Islington, 2007). However, even with the new SEN approach, the EST does not have the resources to give each individual a tailored advice service that is relevant to their own energy use and property.

For this reason (as mentioned above), the Government is now investigating various ways in which householders might directly be given more information on their energy use at home and where the problems lie.

Householders are more likely to take steps to reduce their energy consumption – by changing habits and purchasing decisions – if they have timely, specific and relevant information about their energy use and costs. Consumers save on average up to 12 per cent per year on energy use in these circumstances (DTI 2006a).

At present, home-energy use is metered with almost Victorian technology, in a way that gives virtually no useful information to the householder. For most consumers, information on energy use is given only through quarterly bills, which give aggregated data that cannot be easily related to patterns of use or particular appliances, and which do not give comparisons across time. Often based on estimates rather than readings, these data are in any case frequently inaccurate.

There are three main ways in which more information on home energy use could be given – via bills that tell people more, through 'smart meters' that show patterns of use over time, or by real-time feedback that track energy use second by second.

Information on energy bills
The Government has proposed to mandate improvements in information on energy bills in 2007, requiring comparative historic energy use in graphical form, and supporting information on energy efficiency. A reduction of just 0.25 per cent of household energy use as a result of informed billing would save 0.08MtCe by 2010 (DTI 2006a).

'Smart' meters
Beyond bills, 'smart' meters essentially provide real-time accurate information to householders and suppliers on energy consumption. They have many advantages – they allow remote reading, avoiding the need for house calls, and they provide accurate bills. Currently 25–50 per cent of domestic energy bills are estimated (DTI 2006a). They can be used with variable tariff structures for peak and off-peak rates, and are also capable of having an import–export facility to incorporate microgeneration technologies selling electricity back to the grid.

Together with displays that provide consumers with information about their energy use, such meters have reduced electricity demand by between 5 and 15 per cent because of their influence on people's behaviour (Darby 2006). An estimated 0.2MtCe could be saved in 2010 from better metering and billing (HMT 2006a).

The 2006 Budget allocated £5 million to help co-finance (with energy companies) a pilot study in the use of smart meters and associated feedback devices, with DEFRA contributing a further £4.7 million. The Government believes that full benefits of smart meters cannot be realised without full, national roll-out, but is fearful of the implications for energy prices as the costs of smart meters get passed on to customers. For this reason, it is tentatively exploring developments in this area (DTI 2006a). Results of the metering trials should be available in 2009.

Technology is also now available that can provide householders with real-time information on how much electricity they are using on individual appliances in the house and what it is costing, through a portable display. Powergen will conclude a study in 2007 analysing the effect of deploying such devices in UK homes.

Home Information Packs
Beyond data on levels of use, there are also other types of information that householders can be given on the expected energy performance of their homes overall, and of particular appliances. The most important of these is the Energy Performance Report in the forthcoming Home Information Pack.

Under the European Directive on the Performance of Buildings (EPBD), all homes sold or rented in the UK will have to show an Energy Performance Certificate. This requirement has been incorporated into the

Housing Act, which is bringing in a new Home Information Pack from 2007. The pack will include a report detailing the Standard Assessment Procedure for energy (SAP) rating of the dwelling (a calculation of the building's energy efficiency) and the CO_2 emissions of the property, in certificate form, along with information on how these levels can be improved.

The Energy Performance Certificate aims to draw the attention of prospective homebuyers and tenants to the level of energy efficiency of homes (including new-build and existing properties). This acts in a similar way to the A–G energy-efficiency labelling on white goods, and fuel-efficiency labelling on cars. The focus will be on insulation measures, but will also include microgeneration recommendations.

The hope is that with 1.5m homes being sold each year, the certificates will help influence behaviour at a time when these issues are salient in the minds of the consumer. At the very least, they will provide a good entry point for follow up by energy advice services, such as the Sustainable Energy Network (see above).

The Code for Sustainable Homes

To move environmental sustainability standards for housing beyond the minimum standards outlined in the building regulations, the Government is also introducing a Code for Sustainable Homes – a voluntary agreement setting aspirational standards in energy and water efficiency. The code consists of five levels, with Level 5 requiring homes to be carbon neutral – effectively requiring some form of microgeneration (DTI 2006a).

The code is aimed principally at house builders, but may be used as a marketing tool to influence individual home buyers. Given the extra costs incurred in meeting the higher standards – approximately 6–7 per cent – the number of developers who will choose to build to the higher standards set out in the code is unknown.

It is equally unclear whether consumers will be prepared to pay a premium for homes with higher environmental standards, even if these do involve reduced running costs. In one survey, 45 per cent of respondents agreed that they would be prepared to pay £5–10,000 more for a home built to very high environmental standards, while 29 per cent disagreed (EST 2005a).

Product labelling

Finally, within overall domestic energy use, product labelling has now become an established way of influencing behaviour through providing information on predicted energy performance. The EU energy label has been successful at increasing sales of more efficient appliances, although weak minimum standards have limited their potential effectiveness. The EST also runs the 'Energy Saving recommended' logo, which appears on more than 16,000 domestic products.

Labelling is based on the integrity of minimum standards, but some appliances (most notably, light bulbs) do not have any minimum standards, and are dependent solely on labelling and informed consumer choice.

Efficiency labels appear to be perceived as an indicator of overall quality, thereby influencing consumer choice more widely than through consideration of the impact on the environment or financial savings. There is evidence that they also affect the supply side, since retailers dislike displaying appliances rated in band B or below, creating competition in the remainder of the supply chain (HMT *et al* 2005).

The introduction of A+ and A++ categories to cold appliances has been criticised for weakening the effect of the label, since rather than re-calibrating the bands, the redundant D–G categories were left in place, despite minimum standards making them obsolete, which has caused confusion for customers (Boardman *et al* 2005).

Labelling has also been criticised for the way in which it actually encourages the production of larger appliances, since it is easier to obtain a higher efficiency rating for these appliances than it is for smaller ones, thus reducing the impact on levels of consumption (ibid).

The reason it is easier to obtain higher efficiency ratings for larger appliances is that for fridges and freezers especially, energy labels are based on energy use per cubic metre. It is technically easier to get better energy performance per cubic metre in large appliances, so more of the bigger fridges and freezers tend to be A and A+ rated than smaller appliances. As a result, people go out and buy appliances that are more efficient (per cubic metre) but bigger, and that therefore use more electricity overall.

Contributing to campaigns[8]

The Government's main delivery agent for information on domestic energy efficiency – including through campaigns aiming to change behaviour – is the Energy Saving Trust (described in detail above). With an annual campaigning budget of about £6 million, the EST has run marketing campaigns for more than nine years focusing on raising awareness of climate change and energy use, linking in turn to EST's practical information and support programmes. The 2002 campaign prompted 250,000 people to call EST's energy-efficiency hotline or visit its website.

Various campaign themes have been tried over the years. Early ideas, such as the 'Einstein' branding of energy efficiency as 'the smart thing to do', gave way to campaigns that focused on the financial savings to be

---

8   Information in this section comes from the Energy Saving Trust website: www.est.org.uk and from personal communications with executives at EST.

made. More recently, campaigns have focused on climate change and the need for people to do their bit as part of a collective effort.

The EST's annual flagship event – Energy Saving Week – has been used to launch campaigns and seek to engage the public. This has now developed into a major PR campaign. In 2005, Energy Saving Week generated 45.6 million opportunities to see EST messages in the media.

The current campaign – 'Save Your 20%' – was launched during Energy Saving Week 2004, with a three-year plan to develop consumer recognition of the EST brand, involving public relations activity, television and press advertising, and online activity. During the 2005 campaign, 903 pieces of PR coverage reached 36 million people through television advertising, 38 million through the press and 31 million online, in the largest-ever single consumer engagement campaign.

In terms of consumer awareness and the number of people contacting EST, the 2005/2006 campaign was a success. Calls rose by 68 per cent and website hits by 90 per cent as a result, compared to the 2004/2005 campaign. In addition, the number of calls to EEACs increased sharply, and brand recognition increased by 10 percentage points.

However, it must be borne in mind that these increases are from a low base. Each year, only about 3 per cent of UK households contact an EEAC. Equally, as with the Energy Saving Trust information service more widely, the problem is that impact on behavioural change is both hard to measure and likely to be less impressive than changes in the numbers contacting the EST.

Microgeneration

The Government's aim is to raise the number of households that are producers of energy eight-fold (Brown 2007). Its interventions to increase levels of microgeneration can be summarised as follows.

Regulating consumption

Regulatory interventions in the area of microgeneration have largely been to remove barriers rather than to positively drive behaviour, and have largely targeted obstacles in the planning process. The main area in which regulation plays a role in changing behaviour on microgeneration is in planning – particularly though: Planning Policy Statements; planning exemptions; and voluntary pro-renewables policies.

Planning Policy Statements

Planning Policy Statements (PPS) set out the Government's national policies for different aspects of land-use planning in England. PPS 22 focuses on renewable energy, and aims to encourage local and regional planners to promote and accommodate the development of renewable sources of energy (ODPM 2004b). It explicitly states that size should not be a factor in considering applications, since small-scale projects remain valuable. Hence, it supports community energy and microgeneration proposals.

But these are just guidelines: decision-making remains in the hands of local planners. In fact, 44 per cent of plans referred to government between August 2004 and February 2006 had not put the relevant policy in place, despite it being reasonable to expect the requirement to be applied (DCLG 2006a). The Government is further reviewing how PPS 22 is currently being implemented to urge planning authorities to maximise this power (DTI 2006b).

Planning exemptions

Under the Climate Change Act 2006, the Government is also consulting on putting in place permitted development orders that would effectively exempt householders from the need to seek planning permission to install microgeneration (which is currently a barrier to their uptake).

Voluntary pro-renewables policies

Some local authorities are going beyond what is currently required of them by central government. In 2004, the London Borough of Merton moved to require 10 per cent of energy in new developments to come from on-site renewables. The so-called 'Merton rule' has now been adopted by the Greater London Authority for strategic developments in London and by 19 other boroughs, with many more in the process of adopting pro-renewables policies (London Borough of Merton 2007).

Merton rule-style requirements apply to developers rather than individual householders. However, they may work through to individuals by bringing the price of micro-renewables down as the volume of installations increases.

The Merton Rule will be supported nationally by the Government's forthcoming Planning Policy Statement on Climate Change, which will require that the location and design of new developments should promote carbon-reduction strategies. Measures will aim to promote mixed-use developments, reduce the need to travel, and encourage microgeneration. The PPS is expected to be introduced later in 2007.

Promoting leadership

The Government has not led by example on microgeneration. The use of such technologies by government departments and executive agencies is currently very limited. In its 2005 review of sustainable development in government (SDC 2005a), the Sustainable Development Commission reported that the Department of Trade and Industry was the only government department to use self-generated renewable energy – from photovoltaic cells – and that this initiative contributes only a fraction (0.04 per cent) of the DTI's total energy use (PwC 2005).

Although there is a target for departments to source 10 per cent of their energy from renewable sources by 2008, there is currently no specification relating to on-site renewables. Furthermore, only five departments have made any progress towards the Government's target to source at least 15 per cent of electricity from good quality combined heat and power by 2010 (SDC 2005).

Setting incentives and disincentives

As described in Chapter 5, the most significant barriers to the uptake of low-carbon and zero-carbon microgeneration are cost, and associated long payback times. Not surprisingly then, government policy has so far focused on lowering price. The main approach has been grants programmes, including: the Clear Skies programme; the Major PV Demonstration Programme; the Low Carbon Buildings Programme; and feed-in tariffs.

The Clear Skies programme

From 2003 to 2006, the Clear Skies programme provided capital grants and access to sources of advice for individual householders and community organisations to install microgeneration renewable technologies other than solar PV. On average, Clear Skies funding was equal to approximately 20 per cent of the costs of installation, but was dependent on the choice of technology. A £12.5 million fund provided funding to 8,788 household projects and about 370 community projects, significantly exceeding original targets (EST 2005b, personal communication from BRE to authors, 2006).

The Major PV Demonstration Programme

From 2002 to 2006, the Government provided £31 million in grants for solar PV, through the Major PV Demonstration Programme. This programme funded 1,150 small and individual installations, along with 210 medium-sized and large-scale schemes (DTI 2005a).

The Low Carbon Buildings Programme

2006 saw the end of the Clear Skies Programme and the Major PV Demonstration Programme, and grant support for all renewables was merged into a single Low Carbon Buildings Programme (LCBP), which will run to 2012, and for households is administered by the Energy Saving Trust.

The LCBP aims at a more holistic approach to managing carbon emissions from buildings, by combining microgeneration together with energy efficiency in a mutually reinforcing and complementary way. Grants to householders are for a fixed percentage of the costs, and the scheme will be technology 'blind' – in other words, not favouring any one type of technology – so it is likely that most grants will go to those nearer commercialisation.

The LCBP budget was originally £30 million, £6.5 million of which was allocated to household microgeneration projects. The size of the scheme was enlarged with an additional £50 million of funding, announced in the 2006 Budget. This additional funding will support large-scale demonstration projects (DTI 2005b), with a view to encouraging large actors (primarily developers rather than householders) to enter the market for bulk orders, and thereby (it is hoped) acting as a catalyst for a market transformation (personal communication from Micropower to authors, 2006).

However, after the LCBP had been in operation for just six months, demand for smaller-scale projects was such that the funding scheduled for the first year of the programme had already been allocated, and the DTI has had to provide a further £6.2 million specifically for microgeneration (DTI 2006f). The DTI also introduced a monthly cap on grants, which in March 2007 was met within one hour of the first day, as demand far outstripped the availability of grants. Subsequently, the March 2007 Budget provided a further £6 million for household micro-generation, although it simultaneously signalled that the entire programme of grants for households may come to an end in 2008 (HMT 2007).

In one sense, the micro-renewables grant programmes have been successful, as demand has far exceeded expectations. But in another sense they have not. In particular, so far the schemes have not delivered the scale of installations that will lead to reductions in costs. The Major PV Demonstration Programme caused an annual price reduction of around 7–8 per cent since 2002 – only 2–3 per cent more than would normally be expected through efficiency savings (DTI 2005a). As a result, a sustainable market has not yet been established, and the pattern, timing and degree of uptake of microgeneration technologies remain dependent on grant funding.

Feed-in tariffs

The limited deployment of micro-renewable systems in the UK contrasts with the situation in Germany, Spain and Japan, which have stimulated the uptake of PV and other renewable technologies through a different mechanism – a guaranteed (and generous) price for all electricity generated.

In the UK there is no guarantee for householders that any power exported to the grid – in other words, above and beyond that used in the home itself – would attract any payment (known as 'feed-in tariffs'). Until very recently, only one or two utilities offered their customers these tariffs. This issue is important for payback periods, since a large proportion of power generated in a home installation – especially by PV – is typically exported.

However, the 2006 Climate Change and Sustainable Energy Act 2006 gives the Government the power from mid-2007 to require all energy utilities to offer feed-in tariffs to customers who have microgeneration, and it has signalled that it will use this power if utilities do not make the change voluntarily (DTI 2006a). Furthermore, payments received would not be subject to income tax (HMT 2006a). The Act also includes measures to simplify access to Renewables Obligation Certificates (ROCs) for householders and the Government has subsequently confirmed that any income received from ROC sales will not be subject to income tax or capital gains tax, which should provide a small additional financial incentive to householders. The problem remains, however, that most utilities that now do offer tariffs fail to offer a price for households' exported electricity that matches the price they charge for imported electricity.

Reduced VAT
Finally, reduced VAT at 5 per cent is also applicable to most microgeneration technologies. While this is a welcome display of good intentions towards microgeneration, by helping to reduce the cost of the technologies, the offer is small in relation to the overall cost barrier, and has no discernible impact on uptake.

Providing information
The Government's main channel for information and advice on microgeneration technologies is, again, the Energy Saving Trust.

EEACs merely signpost householders to the Low Carbon Building Programme website, which provides more detailed information, along with a list of approved products and providers that qualify for government grants.

Unlike EEACs, the piloted Sustainable Energy Centres provide advice on renewables directly to householders. However, there is no national campaign in place that specifically promotes the uptake of low- or zero-carbon microgeneration technologies.

Road transport

The Government's interventions to change behaviour on road transport can be summarised as follows.

Regulating consumption
The main areas in which government regulation plays a role in changing modes of road transport are in: planning policy guidance and biofuels.

Planning policy guidance
The growth of the so-called 'great car economy' under Margaret Thatcher

was deeply bound up with a move in land-use planning that took a facilitative stance to US-style trends in industry, leisure and retail to out-of-town developments and, in house building, to low-density suburban sprawl.

On paper, this planning stance changed in the 1990s, and in 2001 the Government brought in Planning Policy Guideline 13, which set objectives for local authorities to deliver on:

- promoting more sustainable transport choices for people (and for moving freight)
- promoting accessibility by public transport, walking and cycling
- reducing the need to travel, especially by car (ODPM 2001).

The planning guidance is not simply focused on improving service provision – it also aims to reduce the attractiveness of car use. Through PPG 13, local authorities are also encouraged to limit car parking in new developments to 1.5 spaces per dwelling, and increase parking charges. The guidance also aims to disincentivise out-of-town developments and promote travel planning alongside planning applications.

Local authorities must take PPGs into account in preparing their development plans, and the guidance may also be relevant to decisions on individual planning applications and appeals, but the degree to which PPG 13 is truly considered and implemented by local authorities is not clear.

Moreover, the Government's decision to endorse key elements of the Barker Review on Land Use Planning (Barker 2006) looks set to reverse policy towards out-of-town developments. The review recommends easing planning restrictions on land next to towns and cities, including green belt land, and a streamlined decision-making process. This could allow a new wave of expansion of retail parks that stimulate greater car use.

Biofuels

The other main area in which the Government is using regulation to influence climate-related behaviour is in the use of biofuels (renewable transport fuels produced from crops). These fuels have the potential to make a substantial contribution to reducing the carbon intensity of transport fuels. CO_2 emissions from biofuels are typically 50 per cent lower than conventional fuels (HMT 2006a), though figures vary up to between 20 and 80 per cent depending on implementation. Sales of biofuels in the UK currently represent 0.25 per cent of total road fuel sales (DfT 2005a).

In 2008 the UK Government will introduce a Renewable Transport Fuels Obligation (RTFO) that requires 5 per cent of all UK fuel sold by volume to come from biofuels by 2010/11. The obligation is not on individuals, but on fuel suppliers, who would earn RTFO certificates for the biofuels they sell. At the end of each year they would be required to declare their total fuel sales and surrender their certificates to show whether they had met their obligation to sell a certain proportion of biofuels. Certificates would be tradable, so that suppliers would alternatively be able to buy surplus certificates from other suppliers to make up their quotas.

Because a proportion of biofuel will be mixed in with petrol and diesel, UK motorists will purchase biofuels unknowingly at the forecourt pumps. While reducing CO_2 emissions from their vehicles, it will not be by personal choice.

Promoting leadership

The main mechanism through which the Government has promoted leadership in order to reduce emissions from road traffic is through voluntary emissions standards – in other words, through agreements with car manufacturers.

For a number of years, the automobile industry has agreed to voluntary emissions standards for new cars at the EU level. Agreements between the European Commission and the European, Japanese and Korean automotive industry bodies (ACEA – European Automobiles Manufacturers Association, JAMA – Japan Automobile Manufacturers Association, and KAMA – Korea Automobile Manufacturers Association) were negotiated in 1998 to reduce the average CO_2 emissions from cars. The agreements have helped drive up the fuel efficiency of new vehicles, but they fall short of the EU's aim to reduce average CO_2 emissions from all new cars to 120g/km by 2010.

The agreed target is to reduce average CO_2 emissions by 25 per cent, from 185g/km in 1995 to 140g/km by 2008. However, progress has recently stalled, because consumers have been buying larger and more powerful models.

Average CO_2 emissions for new vehicles sold in the UK in 2005 were 169.4g/km. To reach the target, a further 15.6 per cent reduction would be required over three years (5.2 per cent or 8.7g/km per annum). This would translate into requiring diesel penetration to reach 50 per cent, low-carbon vehicles (LCVs) to take a 5 per cent market share, and all fuel types to achieve a 5 per cent per annum rate of improvement in efficiency – compared with the 1.1 per cent improvement seen in 2004/05 (SMMT 2006c). This would clearly be difficult to achieve – particularly for the UK, which was ranked ninth out of the 13 EU states for which data is available in terms of fuel efficiency standards for new cars sold in 2005 (ibid).

The European Commission has argued that it would be relatively easy to meet the targets set out in the voluntary agreements. An additional £800 would be added to the average cost of a new car in order to meet a 120g/km target (IEEP *et al* 2005), but this would significantly benefit consumers through fuel-efficiency savings. ACEA concludes that to meet this target via technology alone would cost €400–540 (£273–369) per tonne/CO_2 or

€180–210 (£123–137) per tonne/CO_2 using an integrated approach such as a partnership of stakeholders (SMMT 2006c).

Although it has provided movement in the right direction, the industry leadership approach has not been fully successful. This is partly because, as with appliances, the 'rebound effect' – whereby motorists want ever-larger cars – has more than offset the gains in fuel efficiency.

Hence, in January 2007, the European Commission formally proposed to introduce legislation requiring companies to meet the 120g/km target (130g/km through technology, and an extra 10g reduction through in-car measures such as low-resistance tyres and gear-change indicators, plus further use of biofuels). It is also advocating an improvement of the Labelling Directive for cars, and an advertising code of practice.

Setting incentives and disincentives

The main tools through which the Government has sought to use incentives and disincentives to reduce emissions from road use are: direct taxes on using fuel (fuel duty), on driving (congestion charging), and on keeping a car on the road (Vehicle Excise Duty), investments in infrastructure and services, as well as initiatives to make lower-carbon cars and fuels cheaper, and to promote cycling. Meanwhile, however, the Government subsidises motorised road transport by using money received from general taxation to fund road building.

Fuel duty

Taxation on vehicle fuels through fuel duty has comprised between 58 and 83 per cent of the total cost of unleaded petrol and diesel between 1990 and 2005, but in 2005 was at its lowest rate since 1993 (SMMT 2006b). The controversial fuel-duty escalator, which resulted in automatic tax rises between 1992 and 1999, was scrapped in 2000 following the fuel protests it evoked.

Fuel duty remains a politically sensitive area. Rises in oil prices in 2006 increased the cost of petrol and diesel at the pump irrespective of the fuel-duty freeze, and the Government has used this as a justification for political inaction on increasing fuel duty. While the Government announced that fuel duty will rise again in 2007-2009, it has only been increased in line with current inflation, by 2 pence per litre for 2007 and 2008, and by 1.84ppl in 2009 (HMT 2007) (Consumer Price Index inflation was at 2.8 per cent at the time of going to press). However, between 1999 and 2006, overall prices (measured by the Consumer Price Index) increased by 11.4 per cent, and this will not be reflected in fuel duty.

It is widely believed that progressively increasing the price of fuel through the fuel-duty escalator will force people out of their cars. However, Glaister and Graham (2000) found that increases in fuel prices have only a modest effect on fuel consumption and even less impact on traffic growth.

A price increase of 10 per cent would reduce vehicle kilometres by about 3 per cent in the long term.

Congestion charging
While fuel duty is a broad tax on driving, congestion charging is just beginning to emerge as a tax on driving in certain places at certain times. While a policy aimed immediately at tackling congestion, congestion charging can have an impact on overall levels of car use.

In the UK, only London and Durham currently operate such schemes. The residents of Edinburgh rejected proposals for a scheme following a referendum in 2005.

The London congestion charge was introduced to central London in February 2003 with the aim of reducing congestion, improving bus services, and ensuring the efficient distribution of goods within the area. In 2005, congestion was reduced by 30 per cent from 2002 levels, with a net reduction in car traffic of about 35 per cent (TfL 2006). Traffic changes resulting from the charging are estimated to have led to a 19 per cent reduction in CO_2 emissions from traffic in the congestion zone and a 20 per cent reduction in fuel consumption (TfL 2004a).

The success of the scheme was based in part on the improvements in bus services at the time of the introduction of the scheme, around half of which were directly attributable to the introduction of the congestion charge (TfL 2005). Service provision increased by 22 per cent, and there was a 20 per cent reduction in excess waiting time. Cycling also increased.

Along with promoting a modal shift, the scheme has also been designed to encourage some forms of lower-carbon driving – for example, hybrid cars are currently exempt from the charge. This incentive has been so strong, and the uptake so rapid, that it could potentially threaten the integrity of the scheme. This would appear to be an example of people's desire to avoid paying an additional tax rather than rational, economic decision-making, considering lifetime cost savings.

Initially, public support for the congestion charge concept was low – only 38 per cent supported the scheme, while 43 per cent were opposed. However, following the introduction of the scheme those in favour rose to 59 per cent, while those opposed fell to 24 per cent. The perceived effectiveness of the scheme also rose from 72 to 83 per cent, and the perception of reduced traffic levels rose from 50 to 77 per cent (TfL 2004a).

Thus London's congestion charge has been successful at reducing traffic within a small, but significantly problematic catchment area. The impact on national traffic trends or travel behaviour remains small, although the scheme provides an exemplar for other cities and regions, and in the evolution to national road pricing, to which the Government is committed in principle.

Vehicle Excise Duty

The other main intervention aimed at directly incentivising lower-carbon travel is Vehicle Excise Duty (VED). Since March 2001, VED has been banded according to CO_2 emissions ratings (the only such system in Europe). Initially, differentials between bands were too insignificant to have any influence on purchasing behaviour. Owners of the most gas-guzzling diesel car had to pay just £110 a year more than owners of the most fuel-efficient low-carbon car (Grayling *et al* 2005, DfT 2003c).

In the 2006 Budget, the Chancellor scrapped VED for band A (the lowest emitting category) altogether, decreased VED on bands B and C, froze levels for bands D and E, and increased the level on band F. A new band G, for the most gas-guzzling vehicles, was created for those emitting over $225g/km$ of CO_2. However, the House of Commons Environmental Audit Committee (2006) suggests that the new band G is ineffective, since it currently represents a lower percentage of the vehicle sale price, and works out at half the cost per gram of CO_2 emitted, than the duty for vehicles in band C. Subsequently, in the 2007 Budget, the Government announced further changes to VED, raising the rate for band G to £300 in 2007-08 and £400 in 2008-09; reducing the rate for cars in band B to £35 in 2007-08; and raising the rate for most other bands by £5 in each year for the next three years (HMT 2007).

It is as yet unclear whether this will be a significant enough incentive to significantly affect purchasing behaviour. The expected impact of reforms is quantified by the Government at just 0.1-0.17 million tonnes of CO_2 by 2020 (HMT 2007). Consumer research suggests that differentials of £300 between each band would be needed to cause 75 per cent of new car buyers to swap bands (DfT 2003a).

Interestingly, the history of VED banding contrasts with the banding of company car tax since 2002, which has succeeded in considerably lowering the emissions from company cars. This tax is paid by companies rather than individuals, but it fundamentally affects the vehicles that individuals then drive for all of their needs. Company cars accounted for 55.9 per cent of the UK new car market in 2005 (SMMT 2006c).

Between 2003 and 2004, average emissions from company cars declined by 1 per cent, offsetting the rise from private vehicles of 0.3 per cent. Banding has been tightened since 2002, and differentials will continue to rise from 2008/09, further incentivising the purchase of the newest, most efficient vehicles now available (HMT 2006a).

However, there is little evidence that either fuel duty or Vehicle Excise Duty, at the levels at which they have been set, have been effective at changing behaviour – for example, by making people drive less or buy lower-carbon cars. At this general level, people's attachment to cars is so strong that the existing (admittedly rather mild) economic levers are insufficient to force a modal shift. Only where a defined area of driving is taxed and alternative modes strengthened – as in the case of the London Congestion Charge – has there been a significant impact on behaviour.

Part of the problem is that fiscal interventions would have to compensate for a downward trend in the real cost of motoring. In fact, this cost fell by 5.6 per cent between 1994 and 2004 – mainly thanks to improvements in vehicle efficiency (ippr 2005). In contrast, during the same period the cost of rail fares rose by 5.4 per cent and bus fares 12.6 per cent (Atkins 2005). The price signal currently does not favour the least carbon-intense modes of transport.

Investment in infrastructure and services
An improvement in public transport provision in general is widely believed to be essential for facilitating a major modal shift. Policymakers and the public alike support the provision of improved public transport in order to alter travel patterns. Investing in infrastructure and services is the best proxy for improvements, although the efficiency of expenditure varies.

The 2004 Transport White Paper clearly states the need to invest in public transport to provide alternatives to the car (DfT 2004b), but there has been a legacy of underinvestment in UK transport infrastructure. Investment in rail infrastructure has risen year on year over the past decade, reaching £5.2 billion in 2003/04. However, the rise of £4.1 billion spent on transport between 1994/95 and 2004/05 (HMT 2005) has predominately been absorbed into merely maintaining struggling services. Consequently, services are not perceived to have improved.

Investment in cycling infrastructure, while at a much lower level, has risen. In 2005/06, £45.9 million was forecast to be spent by local authorities outside of London, compared with £29.5 million in 2001/02 – the majority on infrastructure projects such as cycle lanes, advanced stop lines and bike parking facilities. However, in many cases poor quality and ill-designed facilities have meant that cycling levels have not increased in proportion with the quantity of public funding committed to it on a nation-wide level, despite local exemplary success stories and the success of the National Cycle Network (DfT 2005e).

At the same time, the Government is also investing heavily in road transport infrastructure. Public investment in roads was falling until 2000, when expenditure on rail and road were about level at just over £3 billion (DfT 2005a), but has risen again since. This year, the Secretary of State for Transport announced that investment in roads would rise to £1.9 billion for major schemes for 2005/06 to 2007/08, up from £1.2 billion for the previous three years. An additional £300 million was also allocated in 2005/08 for 100 smaller schemes.

Pressure is applied from a local level to spend more on infrastructure for motorists, reflecting the fact that most voters are motorists. Collectively, English Regions would prefer to allocate 72 per cent of their preferred transport budgets to road-related investments and 24 per cent to public transport schemes (Transport 2000 2006). Local government investment in car parks increased by 43.8 per cent between 2000/01 and 2003/04 to £82 million, covering 590km2 of land to provide further facilities for the motorist (DfT 2005a, Living Streets 2005).

Investment in transport infrastructure is frequently cited as a key area in which the Government sends mixed signals to the public on the extent of its genuine commitment to tackling climate change. A vast quantity of government funding continues to be invested in road networks and facilities for motorists. The Future of Transport White Paper (DfT 2004a) planned an extra 900 lane kms of road space by 2010, and 4,032 lane kms by 2025. This is 9 per cent more than what would have occurred under the previous Ten Year Plan, and subsequent emissions will be some 2 MtCe (or 7 per cent) higher in 2010 (Steer Davies Gleave 2006).

Along with expansion of road infrastructure, the Government also currently takes a facilitative approach to speeding on motorways. According to Department for Transport data, more than half the country's motorists exceed the 70mph speed limit, with enforcement often only coming in at extreme speeds of over 100mph or more. Yet driving at no more than 70mph on motorways is probably the most important aspect of eco-driving, representing fuel and emissions savings of the order of 10–30 per cent (personal communication from the Energy Saving Trust to authors, 2007).

While funding for roads has been rising, funding for low-carbon vehicles has ceased entirely. Between 1997 and 2005, the PowerShift grant programme provided £37.5 million of capital support for the purchase of low-carbon vehicles (LCVs). Some 18,800 vehicles were purchased using PowerShift (EST 2004b). However, the scheme's principal aim was to reduce air pollution in general, rather than specifically CO_2 emissions. As a result, there was a technological bias favouring liquid petroleum gas rather than vehicles that emitted the lowest amount of CO_2.

However, the argument used by the Department for Transport for scrapping its low-carbon grants was that as they would only cover 30–40 per cent of the additional purchase cost of such vehicles, they would not achieve market transformation.

Lastly, on biofuels, UK policy towards investing in the infrastructure necessary for their widespread use contrasts with the approach taken in Sweden. There, 12,000 Ford Focus Flexible Fuel vehicles are able to run on any percentage blend, and Bioethanol E85 fuel (an 85:15 per cent bioethanol-petrol mix) will be sold in 25 per cent of Swedish petrol stations by 2008. The infrastructure and vehicles are available to consumers and subject to public choice.

In the UK, the first Bioethanol E85 filling pump was opened in Norwich in March 2006. A further four in the area will follow, with five more in Somerset (LowCVP 2006). Vehicles running on E85 are now officially banded as LCVs and thus subject to the same reduced rates of Vehicle Excise Duty (HMT 2006). E85 retails for 2p per litre less than petrol, but at present the network is not sufficiently extensive to encourage UK motorists to invest in one of the two vehicles available that can run on this type of fuel.

Providing information
The main ways through which the Government has sought to use information to reduce emissions from road use have been through a labelling scheme for new vehicles, and through the Energy Saving Trust.

Labelling for new vehicles
In an attempt to reach consumers directly, a voluntary labelling scheme for new cars was rolled out in July 2005. The colour-coded label displays the VED band and running costs of the vehicle, and identifies its environmental and economic performance. The label takes on a similar form and style to the domestic appliance labels and the forthcoming Energy Performance Certificate in homes, providing a degree of consistency across efficiency labelling schemes.

The impact of labelling on the purchasing of fuel-efficient vehicles is not known. In tests of the impact of the A–G rating system, people responded well to the label in focus groups, but in the showroom car buyers showed limited interest (DfT 2003a). Furthermore, the voluntary nature of the scheme means that many showrooms do not display the car label on vehicles.

The Energy Saving Trust
Despite being the main government-funded body charged with stimulating climate-friendly behaviour, the Energy Saving Trust provides only a limited information service to members of the public on lower-carbon transport options. It does this mainly through its website and not on the whole through its advice centres, except for the new Sustainable Energy Centres currently being piloted, which cover transport as part of a 'one-stop shop' for energy advice for householders.

Contributing to campaigns
Until 2007, there had been no national campaign to encourage the public to adopt lower-carbon transport options. It is notable that the Government has not enabled the Energy Saving Trust to run a national campaign in this area. That is not to say that the Government has been completely inactive. Its main areas of support for campaigns to reduce emissions from road use have been for initiatives on school runs and cycling. In 2007, this was

extended to lower-carbon transport choices.

The school run

The Department for Transport has funded the 'walk to school' campaign, run by Travelwise and Living Streets, which asks parents, pupils and teachers to think about their journey to and from school, and the benefits of making it on foot. The campaign's focus in 2007 is on reducing the pollution (including carbon dioxide emissions) caused by driving to school. Each year, the campaign involves two national events: National Walk to School Week and International Walk to School Month. It also involves the Walk Once a Week scheme, which rewards pupils with an enamel badge if they walk to school regularly. The campaign has the support of over 65 per cent of local authorities and reaches more than 1.5 million pupils and their carers (Walk to School 2007).

Cycling

The Government supports the work of Cycling England, which superseded the National Cycling Strategy Board from its launch in 2005. This is a new national body that coordinates the development of cycling across England, to encourage more people to cycle. In June 2006, Cycling England's budget was doubled to £30 million.

Lower-carbon transport choices

The Department for Transport has now developed a wider communications campaign on lower-carbon transport choices with an emphasis on small, manageable changes. This involves three strands:

- Encouraging the purchase of the most fuel-efficient car within a given class.
- Encouraging smarter (more fuel-efficient) driving
- Encouraging business travel planning to get commuters out of their cars..

Aviation

The Government's interventions to change behaviour on aviation can be summarised as follows.

Regulating consumption

The main area in which regulation plays a role in changing behaviour on emissions from aviation is in planning. The aviation industry (including its ground-based infrastructure) has been entirely privatised, with 95 per cent of investment in airports and air traffic now coming from private sources (DfT 2005a). However, planning control still rests with the Government.

The Aviation White Paper (DfT 2003b) argued that new runways at

Stansted, Heathrow and Birmingham airports would be needed to accommodate growth, along with runway lengthening at Liverpool John Lennon, Newcastle, Teeside International, Leeds Bradford International and Inverness airports. The document also discussed expansion of terminal facilities for a number of other airports. None of the projects referred to were thereby authorised (or precluded), but rather were included in a framework that would inform future planning decisions.

While the Transport White Paper (DfT 2004b) recognised the environmental impact of aviation in the future, it continued to lay out plans to alleviate the pressure of demand on UK airports, through mass expansion. A recent progress report on the White Paper takes the same approach (DfT 2006d).

The Government is looking to carbon pricing and taxation as policies to shape air travel, but continues to take an accommodating approach to predicted growth in airports and runway expansion through the planning system.

Aviation is estimated to contribute £13 billion (2 per cent of GDP) to the UK economy, and the Government maintains that growth in the sector is integral to economic prosperity. Airport expansion is defended on the grounds that people have a right to choose whether to fly or not, and the Government is merely facilitating the possibility of exercising that right.

Setting incentives and disincentives

The main disincentives that the Government has set for flying have been: an increase in air passenger duty; and the EU Emissions Trading Scheme.

Despite the UK Government's rhetoric that airlines and air passengers should pay for the social and environmental costs of aviation, there is no duty on kerosene.

Increasing air passenger duty

At the end of 2006, the Government announced a doubling of air-passenger duty from £5 to £10 for short-haul flights, and from £20 to £40 for long-haul flights in economy, to take effect from February 2007 (HMT 2006a). However, this represents just a 7 per cent increase in the cost of the average short-haul ticket, so it will deter only a relatively small proportion of passengers (Civil Aviation Authority 2005).

The EU Emissions Trading Scheme

The Government has recently supported legislative proposals to bring aircraft operators into the EU Emissions Trading Scheme during Phase II (2008–2012) for flights within Europe (DEFRA and DfT 2005). Additional costs that were incurred from the industry's inclusion under such a 'cap and trade' mechanism would almost certainly be passed on to passengers without their knowledge or as a direct tax.

Preliminary estimates based on modelling suggest ticket prices would increase between zero and €9 (£6) per return flight for any flight departing any EU country (European Commission 2005a). With this level of increase, aviation demand would simply grow at a slightly slower rate than the 150 per cent increase predicted by 2012 (ibid).

Providing information

The main way in which the Government has provided information to reduce the public's contribution to carbon emissions from flying has been through setting up a voluntary Code of Best Practice for air companies providing carbon offsetting to their customers.

In recent years, carbon offsetting has started to emerge as a popular choice among companies and some individuals, for trying to mitigate their impact on the climate – especially for flying, where there are limited technological alternatives. Until January 2007, the Government merely promoted its use through example. DEFRA offset *all* unavoidable carbon emissions derived from its presidency of the European Union and G8, and as of April 2006 will offset *all* emissions from central government air travel (DEFRA 2005).

The Government has now gone a step further, by proposing to establish a voluntary Code of Best Practice for the provision of carbon offsetting to UK customers. The Government's standard would be based on the use of certified credits from the established Kyoto market, through sources such as the Kyoto Protocol's Clean Development Mechanism (CDM). These credits are backed by an international framework and institutions to ensure that real emission reductions take place, as well as providing a clear audit trail.

The Government believes that by providing a standard and code of practice, with a quality mark, people will be given greater certainty that the way they offset is actually making a difference (DEFRA 2007a). However, as the code is voluntary, there is no certainty that companies will adopt it, and on its own, it is unlikely to lead to a significant increase in offsetting. The scheme could also be undermined easily by mixed messages coming from the country's political leaders, such as Tony Blair, who recently admitted that he has not been offsetting his own leisure-related flights (Downing Street 2007).

Having looked at the Government's inputs in the areas of domestic energy, microgeneration, road transport and aviation, we now move on to look at its communications campaigns related to climate change.

Climate-change communications campaigns

The history of climate change communications programmes undertaken by the Government is not an entirely happy one. From 1998 to 2000, DEFRA ran an environmental awareness campaign called 'Are You Doing Your Bit?', with an annual budget of £9 million. The scheme focused on providing information, but was criticised by the Environmental Audit Committee as inadequate, and ended up having little impact on behaviour. Only two people out of ten who were aware of the scheme reported changing their behaviour as a result of it (Darnton 2004a). The scheme was rolled up early, since funds were diverted to tackling the foot-and-mouth crisis.

Some of the lessons from this early experience were drawn into plans for subsequent communications efforts, as DEFRA turned to communications agencies to draw up new principles for climate-change communications (Futerra 2005a). These included recommendations against using approaches that instil fear without giving people the means necessary to act, and against expecting people to act on information alone.

The strategy that emerged from these lessons, and which has driven the Government's subsequent phase of communications, has had two key characteristics:

- It has focused primarily on changing attitudes, not behaviours directly – on the grounds that attitudes towards potential policies and actions for reducing emissions need to change so that the political space and support necessary for their introduction or adoption can be created.
- It has sought to mobilise communications from key actors at local and regional levels as the prime strategy (supported by a few national radio and television advertisements).

In 2006, under the strapline 'Tomorrow's climate, today's challenge', DEFRA has made £6 million available to bids from regional and local organisations for the campaigns, through a Climate Challenge Fund. The result is a wide and diverse range of communications projects, with different audiences in different parts of the country (see Climate Challenge Communication Initiative 2007).

It remains to be seen how effective this campaign will be in changing attitudes. Indeed, with such a small budget available, it will be difficult for the Government itself to assess accurately whether these projects have had an impact. An initial assessment might conclude that it remains invisible, is inadequately funded, and has produced communications that have had very limited market testing and are inadequately targeted. However, it needs to be borne in mind that it has not been designed to have any impact on behaviour directly.

This phase of government communications on climate change is now being followed by an approach that focuses more directly on changing behaviours. In 2007, DEFRA and the Department for Transport will launch campaigns to encourage the public to 'Act on CO$_2$', with websites offering carbon calculators for people to measure their carbon footprints from home energy and transport use, and guidance to encourage specific actions, such as smarter or eco-driving and the purchase of the most fuel-efficient car in a given class.

The Government is also supporting a campaign coordinated by the Climate Group in which different companies will ask their customers to take emission-reducing actions relevant to the companies involved, under the slogan 'We're in this together'. It is too early to say how effective these initiatives will be.

Conclusions

Until very recently, the Government has relied largely on the traditional tools for influencing behaviour that were identified in Chapter 6 of this report – regulation, price incentives and disincentives, and information.

The most consistent element of government policy has been incentives, with price support and VAT reductions for insulation and other domestic energy-efficiency measures, grant support for microgeneration, and variable tax policies to try to push people towards lower-carbon cars, as well as support for alternative fuels.

The problem is that these measures have been rather cautious, limited and weak and this, combined with a very low effective price of carbon, has meant that they have had a limited effect on behaviour. Where a shift in behaviour is taking place – for example, in microgeneration – the scale of the resources that the Government provides (a mere £6 million initially for domestic microgeneration) cannot cope.

By and large, the Government has been reluctant to use regulation to force behaviour change. This approach has been used only in a limited way – for example, through building regulations – and where incentives or voluntary agreements have failed. Interestingly, there is often a preference for schemes with manufacturers or energy suppliers (for example, with the Energy Efficiency Commitment, or the Renewable Fuels Obligation to introduce biofuels) that bypass the need to engage with the public, with the result that consumers can then carry on largely as usual.

In recent years, the Government has done better in providing leadership in terms of the goals guiding the practices and procurement policies of its own departments (although even here, the record is patchy). But its broader policies – particularly in relation to aviation – have not always been consistent with the need to send a clear public signal about the importance of acting to reduce emissions. Above all else, the Government remains wary of calling directly on the public to make specific, large-scale changes in behaviour. When asked whether people should fly less, Tony Blair recently said: 'I personally think these things are a bit impractical... It's like telling people you shouldn't drive anywhere (interview, Sky News, 9 January 2007 – see Downing Street 2007).

This approach may also explain why much of the Government's own communications on climate over the past ten years have focused on changing attitudes to open up the political space for mitigation policies, rather than on behaviour change directly.

Information on how to reduce emissions and standard setting for products has become potentially more useful as climate change has become more visible as an issue. However, the main government vehicle for communicating information – the Energy Saving Trust – is still contacted by only 3 per cent of the public in any one year.

Clearly, a great deal more needs to be done to overcome the barriers to behaviour change. The following chapter argues that behaviour change is actually shaped by the subtle impact of combinations of a diverse range of influences and drivers – some internal, and some external. Consequently, to achieve behaviour change (and hence real reductions in carbon emissions), the Government needs to pursue a much greater range of options for action.

8. What actually shapes behaviour?

To succeed in changing behaviour, the Government needs to apply policies that are based on a realistic understanding of why people actually behave the way they do. From across different disciplines – from anthropology to consumer research, economics, environmental studies, evolutionary biology, human geography, marketing, social and environmental psychology and sociology – decades of research has been conducted, and theories developed, about what shapes behaviour.

This chapter draws extensively on expert summaries of this research – notably by Tim Jackson (2005), David Halpern (2005), Anja Kollmuss and Julian Agyeman (2002), and Andrew Darnton (2004a) – to show that behaviour is influenced by many different factors, in a far more complex process than policymakers have appreciated until very recently. We do not seek to offer a comprehensive account of every theory or model of behaviour formation but to highlight some of the principal influences on behaviour.

Some of the factors that drive behaviours are internal to an individual, while others are external. Both feed off and influence each other, with external factors filtered through an individual's internal perceptions of them. This interaction means that behaviour is often best interpreted from an 'ecological' perspective, which meshes individual factors with wider structural and social ones (Halpern 2005).

The focus in this chapter is largely on some of the internal psychological and external social influences on behaviour, but it is clear that wider structural factors – such as the cost and availability of different choices, and information relating to these choices – can also have an important impact, very often appearing as barriers (examined in depth in Chapter 5). Each influence needs to be taken into account so that effective interventions can be designed to achieve behaviour change.

Internal factors that shape behaviour

The internal factors that shape behaviour include: personal capacities and priorities; meeting of psychological needs; sexual competition and status seeking; construction of identity; morals and emotions; habits and routines; and mental shortcuts. We look at each of these in turn below.

Personal capacities and priorities
It is clear that socio-economic factors, such as how much money we have, how old we are and what life-stage we are in (whether childhood, adoles-

cence, parenthood or retirement), significantly influence behaviour. People are also motivated to pursue behaviours that are in alignment with what is most important to them – their own individual well-being and that of their family (Kollmuss and Agyeman 2002).

Meeting of psychological needs

According to the theory of the hierarchy of human needs, developed by one of the founders of humanistic psychology, Abraham Maslow, people are motivated to behave differently according to their different, unconscious psychological needs.

Maslow maintained that people are first motivated to satisfy material or 'sustenance-driven' needs, such as subsistence (for food, water, oxygen) and safety (comfort, security and freedom from fear) (Maslow 1954).

Once those have been met, he argued, people are motivated to achieve social needs, such as the need for belongingness and love (affiliation, acceptance and belonging) and esteem (competence, approval and recognition). These have been called 'outer directed' needs because the focus of personal identity and self perception is outwardly focused (ibid).

Finally, Maslow proposed that people are motivated to achieve growth-related needs, such as cognitive ones (for knowledge, understanding and novelty), aesthetic ones (for symmetry, order and beauty) and self-actualisation. These have been termed 'inner directed' needs, relating to people's need to know themselves more deeply (ibid).

In later life, Maslow changed his mind about the hierarchical nature of human needs, and placed them side by side instead, in recognition of a duality in human nature (Jackson 2005). Others have since suggested that people can indeed move back from esteem-driven to security-driven modes if their circumstances deteriorate significantly (Rose 2004). However, it has also been argued that once people become inner directed, they do not revert to earlier modes (ibid).

Maslow's theory is of significance to efforts to change behaviours. For decades, Maslow's theory has had a significant influence on how companies persuade potential customers to buy their products and services. Tailoring behaviour-change strategies towards meeting motivational needs is likely to increase their impact, since people's needs play such a large part in driving their behaviour.

Sexual competition and status seeking

Theories of evolutionary psychology maintain that another important influence on our behaviour is sexual competition. Our motivation to beat competition to attract a mate leads us to adopt 'display behaviours'. These are also driven by a desire to establish social status, since a high position within a social hierarchy in evolutionary terms corresponds to improved access to financial, physical, sexual, social and informational resources, which in turn will help protect our individual long-term interests and those of our children (Jackson 2005).

Material goods play a central role in these behaviours (Jackson 2005). So-called 'positional goods' can help position us socially and with respect to potential mates. The more conspicuous the material good, the more it advertises availability, potency and other characteristics desirable to a potential mate – a process from which the notion of 'conspicuous consumption' arises (ibid).

There is probably no more obvious example of a material good that is used to attract mates and maintain social status than the car, which – far from just being a means of getting from one place to another – is deeply imbued with symbolic meaning (Jackson 2005). This theory may also explain why it is so difficult to persuade people to change behaviours that are invisible to our social peers.

Construction of identity

Anthropology and social philosophy suggest that we are also motivated to behave according to how we wish others to think of us, and how we would like to think of ourselves. Once again, consumer goods, such as the car, can play an important symbolic role in constructing our social and personal identity – communicating affiliation to a group or to a set of ideals, and making us think of ourselves in an appealing way. Hence, appealing to people to forgo material goods will often fail (Jackson 2005).

Morals and emotions

People's behaviours are also influenced by their personal moral beliefs or values, which form personal norms to act in a particular way. The 'norm-activation theory' contends that these arise from an awareness of the consequences of our actions, and the ability and willingness to assume responsibility for them (Jackson 2005).

Hence, if we are aware of the impacts of an environmentally harmful behaviour (which are as likely to fall on other people as they are on us) and accept that we have some personal responsibility for that behaviour, we are more likely to develop a personal norm to change it (ibid).

People also behave for emotional reasons that can confound rational self-interest and conscious deliberation. For example, they form emotional relationships with products, and these attachments affect what they buy (ibid).

Habits and routines

Each of us has habits and routines that make many of our behaviours almost automatic, occurring at relatively low levels of consciousness

(Jackson 2005). With routine behaviours, such as boiling the kettle, we may be barely aware that we are undertaking a behaviour that involves active choices at all. Habits are formed through repetition and reinforcement. Especially where habits are associated with an experience of pleasure, they are particularly hard to change (Darnton 2004a).

The way that habits are formed makes the behaviours they affect much harder to alter, despite our best intentions, and less accessible to policy interventions. This is true of many of the everyday behaviours that have environmental consequences, including travel behaviour and decisions related to household energy.

Nevertheless, new habits can be learned by processing information about a specific choice or action, converting that information into a new routine by exercising a different choice, and developing a new 'cognitive script' when the new action is associated with clear positive reinforcement and repeated often over time (Anderson 1982).

Mental shortcuts

We also behave according to a variety of cues that enable us to take mental shortcuts, known as 'heuristics', which reduce the amount of thinking or deliberation that we engage in before acting (Jackson 2005). We use mental shortcuts because there is a limit to how much information we can process, and we need ways of increasing the usability of information. Heuristics involves combining bits of information together, and using rules to make decisions faster and more easily. In some cases, this process can make us prone to misjudgement.

Those seeking to change people's behaviour could benefit from understanding some typical heuristics – in particular, those that can be influenced by cost. For example, as Halpern *et al* (2004) explain:

- We tend to be affected more by loss than gain – hence a fine is a much stronger disincentive than a similar-sized reward is an incentive, and the threat of loss of reputation can be a stronger influence than enhancing reputation.
- We often count short-lived extremes of experience more than average ones.
- We have a tendency to place greater weight on experiences that have just happened.
- We tend to assume that events that we can easily recall or imagine are more frequent, and that they are therefore more likely to happen.
- We often discount the future, giving the immediate more importance than the distant, making it less likely that we will make longer-term investments in our future.

It is worth dwelling on the last of these examples of heuristic thinking, as people frequently apply discounting processes to environmental issues. People commonly see impacts occurring from environmental problems as taking place too far into the future to require them to change their behaviours now. Similarly, they feel that that any differences achieved from behaviour change will only be felt too far in the future to merit change now. They are likely to excessively discount benefits from a behaviour change that are even temporarily delayed, as they will with benefits that are non-events, such as changing diet to avoid a heart attack, or driving less to avoid climate change.

People's tendency to discount the future is a particular challenge for public policy, since there is no ethical basis for society as a whole to discount the welfare of future generations. There is thus an imperative for policy to correct, or address, the problem of individual discounting.

A sense of responsibility and agency

If people are asked to change their behaviour, critical influences on whether they do or not will be:

- whether they have a sense of personal responsibility for the problem that the behaviour change would address
- whether they have confidence in their ability to take action and persist with it
- whether they feel they have the ability to bring about change through their own behaviour.

If people feel their actions will be insignificant, and that change can only be brought about by others, they are unlikely to act (Kollmuss and Agyeman 2002).

The weighting of these internal influences varies by issue, and according to the individual. Each needs to be taken into account to achieve widescale behaviour change. We now move on to look at external factors.

External factors that shape behaviour

External factors that shape behaviour include: what others do; whether we have direct or indirect experiences; and what rewards or penalties we are given. We now look at each of these in turn.

What others do

One of the most important external sources of influence on our behaviours is what others think and do. Research suggests that we learn by example, observing how others behave, and modelling our behaviour accordingly.

Hence, we are influenced and constrained, encouraged or discouraged to act in specific ways by the attitudes and actions of our parents, friends, peers, neighbours, work colleagues, professionals we meet, as well as those portrayed through the media.

This process is particularly influential on physical behaviours – especially if we observe someone experiencing pleasure from them (Bandura 1977). Such modelling plays a key role in creating social norms, which themselves influence people's behaviours in an ever-evolving process (Jackson 2005).

Two types of social norms guide our daily behaviour, and our ability to observe those norms influences the way we are perceived by our peers and our own personal success – for example, in finding a mate, keeping friends and staying in a good job:

- **Injunctive norms** teach us about which behaviours are sanctioned or punished in society. These teach us, for example, that it is wrong to break speed limits or empty our household rubbish onto the street (Jackson 2005).
- **Descriptive norms** teach us about how most people around us behave. For example, it is by observing those on whom we seek to model our identity, or distinguish ourselves from, that we are influenced to buy identity-related items, such as cars, clothes and music (ibid).

Descriptive norms can have a very practical influence. For example, it is not only by reading information but also by observing others around us that we know how, when and where to recycle our waste (McKenzie-Mohr 1999). We also particularly look to the behaviour of others to glean clues about the dominant social norms and give us 'social proof' about how to behave in conditions of uncertainty and crisis (ibid).

Sometimes, people feel pressure to conform to wrongly perceived norms, as with college students who overestimate the extent to which their peers engage in high-risk drinking and increase their own drinking accordingly (Rice 2006). In these circumstances, addressing people's misconceptions can play an important part in changing behaviour.

We do not learn equally from everyone. Social learning theory suggests that we learn most effectively from those who we find most attractive or influential. These vary according to what life stage we are in and what our different psychological motivations are (see above).

During childhood, when it is generally thought that behaviours and habits are formed, the most influential people are our parents, siblings and significant carers, highlighting the importance of early intervention (Halpern *et al* 2004). In adolescence, we are more likely to be influenced by our friends, peers and teachers. At other times, and for certain people, our main influences could be celebrities and people who are successful or powerful, as well as other people who are like us.

We can also learn by counter-example, which means learning how not to behave by observing the behaviour of people from whom we would like to dissociate ourselves, or whom we find inconsistent and so do not trust – people who tell us one thing and do another (Jackson 2005).

It is also important to recognise some of the dominant cultural influences on social norms. These influences often reflect the particular form that social organisation takes within any given society, which, in the industrialised world at least, is still predominantly individualist in nature (ibid).

These cultural influences are also shaped by the media. The factual and fiction-based programming within the media plays an important role in the cycling of the stories and symbolism that help shape behaviour, or are used to justify it. This programming frames or influences the basic worldviews and assumptions that shape the way audiences think (McCombs 1994). Norms are also shaped by commercial organisations, which invest a lot of money and effort in marketing and promoting specific consumer-related behaviours, including through advertising.

All of this implies that if behaviour change is to succeed, effort must be focused not just on the individual, but also on their relationships with those around them, such as their family, peers, neighbours, and the media. For each of the behaviour changes that they seek to achieve, policymakers need to evaluate the role that social norms play in influencing that behaviour, and tailor their strategies accordingly. In many cases, the only solution is nothing less than a transition in social norms.

Whether we have direct or indirect experiences

Research suggests that direct experiences have a stronger influence on people's behaviour than indirect ones (Kollmuss and Agyeman 2002). If a problem can be directly experienced at first hand rather than simply read about or discussed, there will be a stronger correlation between a change in attitudes leading to a change in behaviour (ibid). As a member of a discussion group said when describing her motivations, 'You can read all the books in the world and it doesn't mean as much as actually seeing it happen before your eyes' (cited in Maiteny 2002: 299).

This certainly appears to be the case with the development of 'environmental sensitivity' – defined as a predisposition to take an interest in learning about the environment, feeling concern for it, and acting to conserve it. Childhood experiences of nature and of environmental destruction are among the most frequently mentioned formative experiences that research suggests lead to such sensitivity (Chawla 1998 and 1999, cited in Kollmuss and Agyeman 2002). This may be because experience of the natural world is more likely to generate an emotional connection to the natural environment, and feelings of being part of ecological processes, rather than being separate and insulated from it (Maiteny 2002).

What rewards or penalties we are given

The behaviourist school of psychology argues that any rewards or penalties that we receive following specific actions make us experience positive or negative reinforcements for those behaviours that heavily influence us (Jackson 2005). It contends that many behaviours can be explained through such associations.

The rewards and penalties do not have to be economic in nature, as Pavlov famously demonstrated by succeeding in associating an 'unconditioned stimulus' (food) with another stimulus (the sound of a bell) (Pavlov 1927). Advertisers adopt this approach by associating the products they seek to sell with positively experienced stimuli, such as sexual attractiveness (Halpern *et al* 2004). According to this approach, such techniques can be used to change behaviour by removing existing associations and instilling new ones.

Our behaviours are also strongly influenced by the prevailing incentives, rules and infrastructure that governments choose to (or not to) put in place.

Conclusions

The principal internal and external influences on any given behaviour for a target group of people need to be assessed at an early stage so that interventions can be tailored accordingly for greatest effect.

Until now, policymakers have been good at working with some internal influences on behaviour, such as wealth and age, and some external influences, such as rewards and penalties. But much more could be done to factor in people's different psychological motivations, their drive to seek status and forge identities, the way they get locked into habits and use mental shortcuts to decide how to act, and their need for a sense of agency.

Similarly, more could be done to design behaviour-change strategies that work not only with the individual, but also with their broader social context, so that a more sophisticated use is made of who people learn most from, which norms they abide by, and what type of experiences have the most influence.

With a more complete understanding of how and why people behave the way they do, we stand a much better chance of deploying the most effective tools and techniques available to achieve behaviour change.

9. How has behaviour change been achieved?

Most of us have experienced how difficult it can be to change even a minor habit, so it is not surprising that changing behaviours is very hard. Yet it can be done. Behaviours do change – sometimes very substantially and rapidly.

The response of individuals to recent technological change has been phenomenal, with the boom of the internet, email, mobile phones and air travel. Other profound behavioural changes have occurred as a result of social change – notably, the huge strides made towards ending racial and gender discrimination in the 20th century.

There has also been considerable success in changing some of our other most harmful behaviours. Today, for example, there is overwhelming public support for, and compliance with, the compulsory wearing of seat belts – far removed from the public resistance to their imposition in the 1970s. Drink-driving and smoking have also been reduced, with dramatic changes in social norms occurring. Where once it was unthinkable to ban smoking on aircraft, now it is unthinkable to allow it.

Such successes have not been confined to the industrialised world. Countries such as Thailand and Uganda have achieved significant successes in transforming sexual behaviours to reduce the transmission of HIV.

A common feature of each of these successes is that they were not achieved as a result of a single silver bullet – there is no one-size-fits-all model of behaviour change – but through the deployment of combinations of different interventions at different levels, and by targeting and changing social norms.

These and other successes teach us that traditional regulatory and economic measures, backed by effectively designed communications, can be influential – but they need to be supported by other interventions, based on how people actually behave. A concerted, multi-stranded approach is needed to make sure that the internal and external factors that influence behaviour act synergistically, to reinforce the emergence of new social norms.

This chapter sets out:

- what some of those direct interventions are
- some of the components of effective indirect approaches based on communications.

Direct interventions

The direct interventions that have led to social change have included:

- giving people the choice to behave differently
- making alternative behaviours convenient
- making alternative behaviours appear affordable
- rewarding desired behaviours
- asking people to make commitments to change
- binding people to contracts
- reminding people to behave differently
- providing feedback on behaviour change
- exemplifying change in government and requiring it in the workplace
- involving people in participatory problem solving
- engaging people in behaviour change face to face
- involving people in change at community and group levels.

These are now explored in turn.

Giving people the choice to behave differently

Before individuals can change their behaviours, the new behaviours must be made possible: people must be given the opportunity to choose differently. That means that any physical or infrastructural barriers to alternative behaviours need to be addressed first, before other instruments are applied (Darnton 2004a). The most obvious example of this is that many people, especially in rural areas, will not give up their car unless public transport alternatives are in place.

Furthermore, alternatives need to be seen as being better than whatever they replace. If the infrastructure provided for alternative behaviours is perceived as being inferior, whether in terms of consistency, convenience, comfort, cleanliness, aesthetics or equality of access, then people are less likely to use it.

Where institutions have made attractive alternatives available, responses can be very positive. The University of Washington in Seattle introduced a range of alternative travel options to the car in 1991, including buses, night ride shuttle, can and van pooling and 'ride-matching' (a car-share scheme that helps individuals find other people carrying out a similar commute and matches them up), as well as improved cycling facilities. It simultaneously increased parking rates for cars. The initiative has been enormously successful in shifting commuters away from cars, enabling Washington University in 2000 to meet its targets for its ten-year transportation-management plan (Tools of Change 2007a).

A similar approach has also worked well at the Walton Oaks UK headquarters of pharmaceutical company Pfizer. This scheme involves providing a shuttle bus to the nearby town centre, a daily cash bonus for not using the company car park, better facilities for cyclists, and a car-share database. Pfizer's original 1998 target was to cut traffic in and out of the site by 10 per cent within five years. It achieved it within just two-and-a-half years.

Alternatives need to be consistent and compatible with people's needs, they need to be easy to understand or use, and people are more likely to commit to them if they can try them out first. Similarly, alternative goods or services need to perform at least as well as the ones they are replacing.

Making alternative behaviours convenient

Convenience is a particularly important factor in whether a new behaviour is adopted. Although the concept is viewed subjectively, people usually perceive it as a time-related factor, so that a convenient act is one in which the end justifies the amount of time involved in achieving it (Darnton 2004a).

If even the decision to behave differently is time consuming, people may not change their behaviour, as they are often under time pressure and stress. So, it is important that alternative behaviours, and the methods of choosing them, are convenient. For example, research shows that the single strongest predictor of recycling is access to a kerbside recycling service (Darnton 2004b). Where people have access to this service, household recycling rates go up (Holdsworth and Steadman 2005).

Similarly, critical to the success of the UK campaign for the installation of smoke alarms was a free fitting service by the fire service (together with retailer promotions and television advertising), which led to an increase from 18 per cent to 75 per cent in the number of homes fitted with alarms (Collins *et al* 2003).

The importance that people attach to convenience can also be used to discourage certain behaviours. For example, attempts to change smoking behaviour have made smoking less convenient by allowing smoking only in certain designated places (McDonnell Social Norms Group 2006).

Making alternative behaviours appear affordable

We have already seen that taxation and subsidies can be effective at changing behaviours, by making the behaviours we seek to encourage appear more affordable or cost-effective, and the behaviours we seek to discourage less so. But even when a desired behaviour is made economically viable in this way, people may still not adopt it if it only becomes cost-effective over time – especially if it involves early losses.

This problem can be addressed through smart economic interventions that work with the grain of human psychology, particularly to address people's tendency to discount the future and to dislike losses more than they like gains.

A good example of how this can be done was a three-year trial of a pension scheme in the United States. The scheme worked by deducting a portion of income from an employee's pay rise into their pension. Employees could opt out of the scheme at any time, but few did so, and average pension saving rates rose from about 3 per cent to 11 per cent. It worked well because it avoided disproportionate psychological pain of loss by avoiding asking employees for contributions from existing earnings.

Psychological discounting meant that the loss of future (as yet unearned) income made the contribution feel much smaller. Allowing individuals to opt out also gave them a sense of control, and the company-wide application of the scheme meant that employees became part of it at the same time as all their colleagues, helping create a new social norm (Halpern *et al* 2004).

Another example of successful promotion of a behaviour that would normally involve off-putting upfront costs comes from Canada. The city of Barrie has offered its citizens an interest-free loan to purchase ultra-lowflow toilets and showerheads, to reduce water consumption. The loan is paid off as part of the water bill. As the water is metered, the water saving offsets the costs of the repayments, making the equipment appear effectively free (NEF 2005).

Rewarding desired behaviours

Rewarding positive behaviour can reinforce people's motives to change, and to maintain that change. Rewards do not have to involve cash incentives: they could include anything from personal blood-pressure monitors to meal tickets, training in IT skills, creative writing classes and tickets to local football matches (Holdsworth and Boyle 2004). Ultimately, the reward needs to appeal to mainstream consumers if it is to make a significant impact: it must suit the individual, offering tangible, short-term benefits and needs to be sufficiently visible to draw people's attention to it (McKenzie-Mohr and Smith 1999).

In order to teach people new behaviours and ensure that they become habitual, it is important to make the reward immediate and regular. The reward must not be too small or it will not have any effect; nor must it be too great, or the behaviour will depend entirely on the reward, leaving no room for self-motivation. Finally, the reward provider must be believable and trusted (McKenzie-Mohr and Smith 1999).

One example of a scheme that rewarded people for their efforts to consume more sustainably and motivated them to carry on doing so was the 'NU Spaar-pas Card' ('NU smart card'), in the 1.1 million-strong Dutch city of Rotterdam. The card worked by giving people points for separating waste and buying sustainable products, including energy-efficient goods, bicycles and renewable energy (for which they received four points per Euro spent). People could then spend their points on sustainable products, public transport, or leisure activities in the city such as going to the cinema, the swimming pool or the zoo.

The scheme was set up and supported by the Rotterdam Municipal Authority, Rabobank, the European Union and the Province of South Holland. Marketing experts sold the card to shops as a loyalty scheme to boost profits by attracting and retaining customers, while consumers were targeted through mass mailings and publicity in the papers, radio, television, posters, magazines and flyers. The scheme operated from May 2002 until January 2004, during which time it involved 10,000 cardholders (Holdsworth and Boyle 2004).

Asking people to make commitments to change

Asking people to make a commitment to change their behaviour, whether at an individual, household or community level, has been shown to reinforce intentions to change, and to promote a sense of responsibility to do so, with surprising success. For example, studies show that people who have simply been asked to watch over someone else's property are 400 per cent more likely to try to stop a theft than those who are aware of the theft but have not been asked (Halpern *et al* 2004).

Commitments work most powerfully when they are made publicly – when people make them to other people, rather than to websites or to themselves – and when they believe that the commitment means something to the person to whom they are giving the commitment (Futerra 2006).

During the energy crisis of the 1970s, participants in a programme in the US city of Iowa were divided into two groups – one making a public commitment to reduce energy use, and the other just a private commitment. The group making a public commitment subsequently cut energy consumption by 10–20 per cent, contrasting with the other group, which did not reduce energy use at all (Pallak *et al* 1980).

Commitments are thought to work for several reasons. First, they can help raise habits from unthinking automaticity (knowing how to do something so well that you do not have to think about it while doing it) to discursive consciousness, helping unfreeze, break and reform them. Also, the act of agreeing to do something often alters the way we think of ourselves – we come to see ourselves as the type of person who believes it is important to act in a certain way. Making commitments, especially publicly, strengthens the feeling of how we should behave, and the shame we feel if we fail to live up to those commitments (NEF 2005).

In addition, we have a strong desire to be seen as consistent by others, and this is reinforced by a social norm which views negatively people who are inconsistent. Hence, if we were to wear a badge supporting the purchase of a particularly type of product, we are more likely to want to purchase that product when we shop than to be viewed as inconsistent (McKenzie-Mohr and Smith 1999).

Written or signed commitments have been found to be more effective than verbal commitments, with publicly made commitments more effective than those made privately. Findings also show that groups of people who are highly cohesive are the most likely to adhere to a commitment, because their close ties makes it more likely that the individuals will follow through. It is also effective to use existing points of contact such as a retail store to obtain commitments (McKenzie-Mohr and Smith 1999), and it is recommended that the commitments are monitored in some way to make sure they are honoured (Nigbur et al 2005).

Commitments that involve goals can give people something against which to measure success as they progress. This can increase people's sense of self-efficacy, as can setting small incremental goals that are stepped up over time: when people achieve their first small goal, the next one seems more achievable and they are more likely to persist (Halpern et al 2004).

A long-standing example of the use of commitments is the Norwegian Environmental Home Guard programme's Eco Pledge initiative. Here, households sign up to undertake a number of sustainability-related actions, and are supported in their endeavours through postal, email and personal contact. Since 1991, 100,000 people have signed up as well as half of Norway's local municipalities (Holdsworth and Steadman 2005).

Similarly, in Canada, the Government asked individuals, households, groups and communities to sign up to the 'One-Tonne Challenge', to achieve a 20 per cent cut in the annual greenhouse gas contribution of the average Canadian. The initiative was publicised through a dedicated website, a published guide (sent to 900,000 Canadians in the first year), advertisements, exhibits, and community-based partnerships, in order to: explain the need for the challenge; provide examples of the challenge being successfully met; circulate tools to measure household emissions; and offer information about how to reduce these emissions, including links to rebates available and other incentives.

The initiative was launched in March 2004. By March 2006, 83,000 Canadians had taken the pledge (Government of Canada 2006).

Binding people to contracts

Contracts provide a more formalised process to set goals, and specify rewards and penalties on the basis of behaviours undertaken. They make explicit what is expected of whom, and can foster a shared and mutually reinforcing understanding of rights and responsibilities (Halpern 2005).

Welfare to Work is one widespread example of the use of contracts. Through this scheme, individuals receiving unemployment benefits are expected to look for work and take work or training that is available or face losing their benefits. Similarly, they are used by doctors to encourage healthier behaviours, by police and local authorities to reduce anti-social behaviour, and by schools to increase attendance and discipline. In the United States, graduation incentives are paid to students in exchange for their staying on in school (Halpern et al 2004).

Contracts have also been used to promote pro-environmental behaviours. In Denmark's second-largest city, Arhus, the municipality asked participants in a sustainable transport project to sign a contract committing them to reduce their car use, and to use bicycles or public transport instead. They were given a bicycle for one year and a bus pass worth over £450. Ninety per cent of the participants in the project fulfilled the contract.

During the project, the percentage of trips made by bicycle increased from 9 to 50 per cent. After the project ended, most participants maintained the change, with 40 per cent of trips conducted by bicycle.

In this example, the use of contracts helped unfreeze entrenched travel habits, breaking and reforming routines – aided by the provision of significant incentives (Holdsworth and Steadman 2005). However, overuse of conditionality can undermine the value of any possible intrinsic rewards offered by a behaviour that may drive self-motivation.

Reminding people to behave differently

Many new behaviours – particularly new habits – are susceptible to being simply forgotten. This is certainly the case for behaviours that are desirable for environmental reasons. Prompts, in the form of visual or auditory aides, can be effective in reminding people to carry out an activity that they might otherwise forget.

In order to be effective, prompts need to be noticeable, eye-catching, self-explanatory, and placed close to where the action is to be taken. Prompts to encourage people to engage in positive behaviours are more likely to be supported by retail outlets, and they make people feel good about their actions – which, in turn, increases the likelihood that they will be carried out in the future (McKenzie-Mohr and Smith 1999).

A good example of the effectiveness of prompts is the presence of green recycling boxes or bins, which studies have shown remind people to recycle when they would not have otherwise thought to do so (Darnton 2004a). The act of putting a green box out for kerbside collection also exerts social pressure on other residents.

Another example of effective prompts comes from a programme run by Canadian NGO EnviroCentre to promote sustainable travel behaviour in the late 1990s. Alongside traditional information provision, the programme used prompt cards and a memo holder to remind people of the steps they could take. Between 25 and 50 per cent of those in the programme reported changing travel use away from car use. Ninety per cent of participants kept the prompt as an ongoing reminder (Tools of Change 2007b).

Providing feedback on behaviour change

Communicating feedback and praise on performance or progress made can also be effective – particularly in relation to behaviour changes that will have only long-term benefits (McDonnell Social Norms Group 2006). Feedback helps because it can reduce a person's anxiety about their ability to change, and may increase their perception of themselves as the type of person who would act in the desired way, thus reinforcing their motivation to persist.

Publicising feedback about a behaviour change can also help make desired social norms appear visible, increasing the impact on others. And it can have a greater effect on the learning process if it occurs soon after the action involved (Jackson 2005).

Asking people to provide their own feedback by self-monitoring can also bring an activity out of the realm of habit into the realm of discursive consciousness, which is critical to being able to change it. For example, in schemes to encourage people to use their cars less, researchers have asked volunteers to keep travel diaries, to monitor which journeys could be made by other means (Halpern et al 2004).

Comparative feedback may be particularly beneficial – especially at a very local level, where it can be used to make meaningful comparisons and generate competition in the desired activity, with for example, explicit recognition being given to streets or communities that are leading the way or falling behind.

Households in the Surrey Scholar Research Project on recycling for Guildford Borough Council received feedback slips through their letterboxes on recycling day. These told household members:

- if participation in the neighbourhood was better or worse than another neighbourhood
- whether the number of households participating in kerbside recycling in their neighbourhood was higher or lower this week compared to two weeks ago
- whether or not their neighbourhood had achieved a specific target for recycling participation (Nigbur et al 2005).

The results showed that this feedback greatly influenced residents' participation, in the scheme – particularly when comparisons were made between a household's own street and the street showing the highest participation in the area. The highest increase in kerbside recycling was among those who were told that their neighbourhood was doing worse than another. In one street, recycling rates increased from 51 per cent before feedback to 90 per cent afterwards (Nigbur et al 2005).

Feedback was particularly effective at encouraging non-recyclers to participate. This group responded especially well to feedback stating that their neighbourhood had recycled more than others, or had exceeded a fixed target. This is thought to be because such feedback makes people feel successful at recycling, and hence encourages them to develop a self-image as a 'recycler'. Once people identify themselves as a recycler, recycling is thought to become self-sustaining (ibid).

Exemplifying change in government, and requiring it in the workplace

The example given by government can play an important part in achieving behaviour change. Jackson (2005) argues that aligning government policies, management and procurement practices with the behaviour changes that the public is being asked to make sends out strong signals that:

- the Government is serious about achieving change
- this change is a national priority
- the change is possible.

It can also subtly but powerfully influence social norms, by indicating what behaviours, attitudes and goals are rewarded and valued in society (Jackson 2005).

Central government can also provide guidelines to providers of contracted-out services, to schools, hospitals and other services run by local authorities, and to companies, to help ensure that they too exemplify the behaviour change that is sought.

In attempting to change behaviours, it is important to think of consumers in their roles as employees too – whether in the public or private sector. In our workplaces, for example, we are exposed to environmentally significant practices relating to waste, water and energy use, as well as travel and procurement practices. If we are encouraged to adopt pro-environmental behaviours at work, we will become familiar with specific actions and encouraged to think of ourselves in a different way, making us more likely to adopt those behaviours at home.

The more that behaviours are repeated, reinforced and normalised, by being incorporating into everyday life, the faster new habits and social norms will be created (Kollmuss and Agyeman 2002). On the other hand, if employees are not encouraged to adopt new behaviours at work, this can significantly undermine the incentive for consumers to adopt them at home (Jackson 2005).

For example, bans on smoking in the workplace and in other public spaces have helped change social norms and reduce the incidence of smoking. However, these have taken place alongside a range of other measures, including taxation, advertising bans, health warnings on packaging, powerful communications, education strategies involving community groups, schools and other organisations, and access to treatment.

It is not only in workplaces that influence can be exerted over behaviours. Schools, too, can play an important role, by requiring or encouraging desired behaviours in pupils and staff. This type of behaviour change is being encouraged through 'Play it Cool' – an initiative from the Global Action Plan (GAP) and the Centre for Sustainable Energy. This scheme provides practical support to schools in London and the South West to use energy more efficiently. GAP staff guide a team of students, teachers, non-teaching staff, parents and governors to measure the school's energy use, and to set its own improvement targets and action plan. Curriculum-based support materials help teachers incorporate the messages into lessons (GAP 2006).

Involving people in participatory problem solving

Involving people in participatory problem-solving processes can help people overcome important barriers to behaviour change – notably, a lack of agency from the perception that they cannot make a difference, and a lack of trust in what is being asked of them (Jackson 2005).

Engaging people in problem solving can make them feel more competent and empowered to make a difference (NEF 2005), and increases trust in outcomes (Collins *et al* 2003). It also ensures that the quality of policy-making is improved. It is more effective than telling people what to do, which can be demotivating, provokes resistance, and ignores the possibility that people's own knowledge may yield better solutions.

Deliberative processes need to be used that help people understand the issues and the trade-offs, and to invite them to come up with their own ideas and solutions, supported and guided by experts and government, in a partnership to negotiate behaviour change. People need to be seen as potential partners in the 'co-creation' of policy, instead of passive 'respondents' (Trayner 2006, Cottam and Leadbetter 2004). When such opportunities have been provided, consumers have shown an ability to think through complex issues and demonstrate imaginative responses (ibid).

These principles have been applied in a wide range of policy and public service areas, including health, school design and ageing (Winhall 2006). In efforts to tackle chronic health problems such as diabetes and obesity in the UK, large deliberative workshops on policy are one of a range of techniques being deployed to get patients to take more active participation in the provision of services. This 'co-creation' approach also includes face-to-face experiences delivered through social enterprises to motivate exercise, and methods for personalising communication between diabetes specialists and their patients.

Deliberative processes should not be one-off events, but rather ongoing conversations with the public over time. These can yield greater insights and give people a greater sense of recognition for their contribution. These conversations can be carried out through follow-up telephone conversations, online forums, reconvened workshops or small committees set up to meet after the initial deliberative event to audit the conclusions drawn and recommendations made (Trayner 2006).

Engaging people in behaviour change face-to-face

Nothing is more effective in delivering a message than personal contact (UNEP 2005a), and in some policy areas face-to-face approaches have been shown to be very effective in changing behaviour. Studies show that face-to-face communication allows the development of trust, minimises misunderstanding, and allows other sensory communication methods to work interactively (Cooke 2003). Personalisation of contact is also important because each of us is different, and wants to be treated in a way that reflects this. Some commercial organisations have learnt to adapt to customer needs, and public services need to emulate the most appropriate commercial practice available.

After an initial approach by telephone or letter, home visits can be arranged by project personnel to enrol a participant in a scheme, provide information, help them identify ways of changing behaviour, or seek a commitment from them. Opportunities can also be created for people to talk to one another – so that, for example, individuals in a neighbourhood who already have experience in a sustainable activity may speak about it to others who live close by.

Home visits, along with the impact of direct experience and rewards for behaviour change, have played a crucial role in Canada's highly successful EnerGuide for Homes programme of energy-efficiency retrofits. Trained energy assessors conduct an initial home visit and take householders through a pressure test on their home (which establishes the rate at which air is able to move through a building under pressure), providing a dramatic demonstration of the leakiness of their property. The face-to-face contact builds trust, and helps motivate action by the homeowner. The EnerGuide programme has targeted hundreds of thousands of homes in Canada.

In an experiment with 30,000 voters in the US, face-to-face reminders of a forthcoming election proved far more effective than leaflets and telephone calls in boosting turnout (Halpern *et al* 2004). In Perth, Australia, door-to-door visits have also been effective in encouraging people to use their car less (ibid).

Another example that demonstrated the impact of home visits, combined with other types of interventions discussed earlier, was an initiative in Durham County, Ontario, to reduce garden water use. Some householders were visited by an employee, who spoke to residents about efficient water use, and provided them with a water gauge and a water-saving prompt and asked them to sign a water-saving commitment. Residents in this group decreased their watering by 54 per cent. In contrast, those in the control group, who were only posted information, increased lawn watering by 15 per cent (McKenzie-Mohr 2000).

Involving people in change at community and group levels

Behaviour change can take place more effectively, and last longer, if communities and voluntary or professional organisations are empowered to work with individuals to negotiate change (Halpern 2005). Community groups are closest to people's everyday interests and needs, and the public is more likely to trust the information that these groups can provide on behaviour change than information from government, since we are more likely to tend to trust people who we know, or can get to know. Community groups can be set up by local government and campaigning organisations, within religious organisations and workplaces, or by neighbours.

Community groups can give individuals the personal and practical support they need to change their behaviours. They can sustain individuals during the considerable period of time during which learning takes place and behaviours actually change, by providing validating feedback on behaviour change (Ballard 2005).

Groups can be especially helpful in providing the supportive social environments necessary for 'unfreezing' existing behaviours and habits. They do this by raising the behaviour to the level of discursive consciousness, so that low-level everyday actions are raised up to scrutiny in an open and supportive way (Jackson 2005). They can foster the sense that a new way of behaving is the social norm, and maintain that changed behaviour until it becomes a habit (Darnton 2004a).

Group working is also particularly valuable in enabling people with a lower sense of personal agency to change behaviours (ibid). We often feel isolated and lacking in agency when we try to change behaviours on our own. Being a member of a group can make us feel we are not the only drop in the ocean but one of many who, together, can make a difference (Maiteny 2002).

An effective approach to community-level strategies to achieve behaviour change is community-based social marketing, which uses tools and techniques based on social and psychological theories. This approach encourages people to develop dialogue with other members of the public, and to forge durable relationships built on trust to gradually increase people's willingness, confidence and capability to make large-scale changes in behaviour (Halpern *et al* 2004).

Community-based social marketing also encourages a systematic approach to changing behaviours. It first involves deciding which behaviours most need changing, because resources rarely exist to foster change in a wide range of areas. It takes into consideration the impact of different behaviours on a given problem, the barriers that exist to changing those behaviours for different people, and which are the most important.

It reviews what the most effective tools and techniques would be (some of which are described above) to overcome those barriers, and whether the resources exist to deploy them. Its conclusions should then be tested with members of the public, through focus groups, surveys or observational studies, before strategies are piloted, evaluated, and – if successful – more widely implemented.

Global Action Plan (GAP) is a leading example of an organisation deploying the community-based social marketing approach. It is achieving high levels of success through group-level behaviour change management, helping bring about tangible changes in people's environmentally-related behaviours (Darnton 2004b). Since 2004, GAP has established 800 'EcoTeams' in England. EcoTeams consist of groups of people representing six to eight households. They could be neighbours, members of the same religious or interest group, retired people, young people, parents or work colleagues.

Members meet on a monthly basis and share ideas, experiences and achievements. They follow a step-by-step programme, based on a workbook that sets out goals and actions that can be taken by households to address sustainability-related issues and form new habits. Team members measure their household's gas, electricity and water consumption so that improvements can be monitored and results shared. The programme takes four months to complete, and support is provided to each team by a coach or a reporting centre (Jackson and Michaelis 2003).

EcoTeams have typically achieved reductions in car use and in energy of 10 per cent (ibid). Some have achieved much more: the EcoTeam programme in Rushcliffe in Nottingham achieved 27 per cent savings on gas and electricity in 2002 (GAP 2006). Other group projects have had similar a success, including EST's 'Café Community' projects, which have helped deliver three times greater energy saving than non-community groups (Environment Agency 2006).

The challenge for this approach is to make it more inclusive, so that the less advantaged or proactive are not left out (Darnton 2004b). For this reason, GAP has also introduced behaviour-change programmes designed for low-income consumers. Ways also need to be found to multiply the number of these labour-intensive programmes, so that a significant portion of the population can be covered.

Designing effective communications

As we saw in Chapter 6, the evidence suggests that the use of mass communications to increase knowledge and shift attitudes may have a role to play in increasing levels of awareness of a problem, and in increasing acceptance of the need for new policy initiatives to remedy it. But it will not lead to behaviour change on its own.

The value of communications in relation to behaviour change lies in its ability to assist, complement and reinforce policy measures, and the provision of infrastructure designed to incentivise the public to take action. If behaviour change is the objective, governments should only expect communications campaigns to be useful if they simultaneously introduce policy measures alongside it that encourage people to consciously engage with, and act on, the subject matter of the persuasive message (Jackson 2005).

If that approach is adopted, there is a strong case for efforts to be focused on communicating practical information about how specific behaviours can be changed – one behaviour or action at a time – spelling out what consumers can do themselves, how, why, where and when. Without that, other measures to drive behaviour change may not work (Darnton 2004a). A good example of such an approach on climate change is the Canadian government's 'One Tonne Challenge' campaign, under the Climate Change Action Fund (see above).

Beyond that, there are important ways of designing communication approaches that will increase their effectiveness in a very message-dense environment, but these have not always been adopted in the past. The first of these is the need for all communication campaigns to have clear objectives and a thorough research and development phase that involves the public at its heart.

Knowing and segmenting your audience

The most successful communications campaigns and behaviour-change strategies tightly define their target audiences (UNEP 2005b). Governments traditionally like to reach a very wide audience, but it is a mistake not to tailor messages (as well as messengers and communication channels) to specific audiences, as different groups have different capacities and motivations, and face different barriers.

This means that understanding the differences between subgroups of the population is essential. In particular, those running the campaigns need to know their audiences sufficiently well to be clear about what will motivate them to make changes, so that they can target interventions appropriately. Understanding what motivates an audience is the first step to knowing how to talk to them (ibid).

Audience segmentation systems such as MOSAIC and Acorn, which rely on consumer lifestyle, attitudinal and socio-economic data can tell us a lot about different audiences. But to improve their ability to impute motivations, they would benefit from being complemented by psychographic models.

For example, a consultancy called Cultural Dynamics has developed the 'values modes' segmentation model, which draws on Maslow's theory of psychological needs and can segment any sample of the population into three broad 'motivational groups', which in turn are divided into 12 more finely-tuned subgroups. These are related to 70 attributes, based on answers to a questionnaire involving hundreds of questions.

This system can track the values, beliefs and motivations of generations of people, using data from 33 years of psychological studies in the UK. This allows anyone seeking to change behaviours to improve the way they craft their approach, on the basis of a psychological understanding of what motivates different people to behave in different ways.

This knowledge can be used to complement their understanding of the practical issues and the barriers that motivate them. For example, efforts to promote pro-environmental behaviour would benefit from understanding that 'esteem-driven' people may best be engaged by designing propositions that are fashionable, high-impact, low-risk ways of being 'green' through lifestyle and purchasing options, or by naming and shaming (Rose 2004).

Box 9.2: Understanding the psychological profile of your audience

The cultural dynamics values modes segmentation model draws on Maslow's theory of psychological needs to identify three broad motivational groups. According to this approach, each group will respond to propositions according to whether or not they meet their needs and whether they make 'common sense' to them. The groups are as follows:

Group 1: Pioneers Pioneers make up 35 per cent of the UK population. They have inner-directed needs, including needs for an ethical basis for life and self exploration. They seek meaning in life and new truths, and look forward, both in time and to new horizons. They like change, discovery and the unknown, and are unworried about status.

Pioneers tend to believe in some greater purpose to existence. They determine their family structure according to 'what works', and possessions on display in the home will tend to have some intrinsic aesthetic appeal or other personal significance. They need a degree of ongoing variety and change in their lives, as well as adventure and challenges, and they pick up different kinds of knowledge for its own sake.

Pioneers tend to be more causal about finances than their peers, and see the purpose of money as being to buy quality. They are the dynamic of society, laying out new routes through life. Where they go, others – particularly prospectors (see below) – tend to follow. Already representing over one third of the UK population, this group will grow over the next 40 years as more people satisfy their outer-directed needs.

Group 2: Prospectors Prospectors make up 44 per cent of the population and have esteem or outer-directed needs. They live 'in the now', for today, and seek rewards in terms of fashion, status, success, achievement, recognition and esteem of others, and are unconcerned with belonging, security or identity, because they have that already.

They could be said to be highly materialistic, seeking success through acquiring, consumption, displaying the 'right' brands and fashionable lifestyles. Their need is to make their success visible, and the most common showcases for this are the home (possessions and decor), the car (top brand) and the holiday destination (as exotic as possible). They like earning and spending money, and see the world as a big opportunity. They tend to be ambitious: position and power are important to them.

Prospectors are a diverse group in socio-economic terms, but are most strongly represented by middle-income women and teenagers. In the past 25 years, this group has been the largest and fastest-growing group, representing almost half the UK population. This approach to life drives the consumer economy and is magnified by the media, so it could be said to set the background tone to society.

Group 3: Settlers Settlers make up 21 per cent of the population. They have sustenance-driven needs. They tend to look backwards, to yesterday (which was better), and dislike anything new or different, as this threatens identity and their sense of belonging, security and safety.

Settlers are motivated by the need to protect and hold on to what they have. They believe that rules should be respected and obeyed. They have what could almost be termed 'traditional values'. Their home is where the heart is, and tends to have a comfort focus to it, in a physical, emotional and psychological sense. They like to socialise with people like them. Financial security is of high importance, and money is spent cautiously. They may resist change – potentially vocally. Routines provide islands of certainty in their lives.

Their role in society is to provide the brake that will stop the train from hitting the buffers. This was once the largest group in British society, and largely defined the present culture, but it has been in steady decline since 1945 and is now the smallest group. While there is a measurable bias in this group towards people at the lower end of the socio-economic range, a significant proportion at the other end of the spectrum demonstrate the same characteristics.

Source: Adapted from Dade and Rose 2005

This approach has been employed by a number of organisations, including large corporations such as Unilever and Shell, public institutions, such as the BBC, and political parties, in more than 40 countries. It is not a substitute for traditional audience segmentation based on socio-economic indicators such as age, gender, wealth and life-stage, but should complement it. Indeed, industry has combined these two approaches since 1973 (personal communication from Pat Dade of Cultural Dynamics to authors, 2007).

Understanding when different groups of people are most open to change can also make communications more effective. Identifying when people are in transition – when they are moving home, getting married, having a child, or retiring – can usefully influence the timing of communications, as these are moments when people's habits and routines are most in flux.

It has also been suggested that communication campaigns should target and engage 'key influencers' or 'protagonists' who are more than averagely connected and, it is contended, play an important role in rapidly spreading messages through social networks (Darnton 2004a). A variation on this theory is that of 'the new persuaders' who, it is claimed, are skilled at making friends and know a wide variety of people, are persuasive, are good information gatherers, and have a significant impact on 'the perceivers' who represent the majority in society (OLR 2003).

This process is the basis for the 'tipping point' theory, in which small numbers of key people can have a big impact in little time (Gladwell 2000). As yet, there is little evidence base to support these theories.

Crafting messages and concepts effectively

Knowing your audience enables communications approaches to be developed that will work specifically for them. A US campaign to discourage people from buying fuel-inefficient sports utility vehicles targeted religious networks, using the slogan 'What would Jesus drive?'. Another US campaign to decrease litter on the Texas highways, having identified their target audience as young men of between 15 and 24 years of age, developed the slogan 'Don't mess with Texas'. The goal was to associate the idea of cleaning up litter with something the target audience already believed – that being from Texas is somehow special (Fenton Communications 2001).

Every communications campaign needs to be crafted to meet its own specific objectives, but there are some general, obvious, commonsense rules for developing messages and concepts (other than audience segmentation) that effective communications need to apply (Futerra 2005a and 2006, Fenton Communications 2001, Schellenberger and Nordhaus 2004, Ereaut and Segnit 2006), including:

- *Keep messages clear and simple, and do not preach* Little is more effective at turning people off than over-complex information or a sense of being lectured.

- *Use personal and emotional appeal* Connect with what matters to people in a way that engages with their feelings. People need to be reached emotionally first, and then informed ('hearts then minds'). One way to do this is to use what people can empathise with – usually people and animals, rather than landscapes. It is also important to reach people in as personal a way as possible, with messages about their region, their town, their street, their house, themselves.
- *Use the power of image* Visuals can have a much bigger impact than words – not just in depicting problems, but also in showing solutions.
- *Make behaviour changes aspirational* Link the issue, product or change in behaviour that is sought to the aspirations of the target audience. This can be done by finding out what is attractive about the change of behaviour, and associating these characteristics with aspirations for the home, family and self – such as the desire for health, well-being, wealth, jobs or comfort.
- *Give people an inspiring aim* Offer people a positive, transformative vision. Imagine how history would have turned out if Martin Luther King had given a speech saying 'I have a nightmare' instead of 'I have a dream'. Yet, much communication on environmental problems effectively gives the 'I have a nightmare' speech on a regular basis.
- *Don't create fear without agency* If the message is too negative it destroys the perception that something can be done, and creates apathy. Only contemplate a threatening message if it is possible to simultaneously present concrete actions that individuals can take to reduce the threat. In those circumstances, communicate on the basis that people are more concerned about threats they can easily imagine, and will discount those that are too general and distant.
- *Make sure communications avoid making people feel bad, irrelevant or useless* People want to feel good, important and useful. Communications need to convey a genuine sense that large numbers of people are acting, and to show the impact that individual actions can have at the collective level. This helps individuals feel that they will not be acting alone, that what they are doing is 'normal', and that it can make a difference. That means making the 'good' sound 'normal' and the 'bad' sound rare.

Applying strategic frame analysis

Another important approach to the development of communications is the use of 'strategic frame analysis'. This approach, based on research into how people think and communicate, is centred on the concept of 'frames'. Frames are conceptual structures used in thinking, and are realised in the brain by neural circuitry. Every time a frame is evoked by a word or an image, a neural circuit is activated and the frame strengthened (Lakoff 2003).

Frames can be thought of as what Walter Lippmann called 'pictures in our heads', or scripts, which we have learned since childhood to help us make sense of the world (Lippmann 1921). They enable us to make mental shortcuts, in order to process incoming information quickly and efficiently. When we receive new information through language or images, cues within that information signal to us how to classify or assimilate it into the frameworks – the concepts or values – that exist in our heads. This allows us to accord that information with meaning (FrameWorks Institute 2001). Simply put, it involves 'finding a story you already know and saying, "Oh yeah, that one"' (Schank 1990: 71).

How an issue is 'framed' – what words, metaphors, stories and images are used to communicate about it – will therefore determine what frames are triggered and which deeply held worldviews, widely held assumptions or cultural models it will be judged against, and it will then be accepted or rejected accordingly. If the facts do not fit the frames that are triggered, it is the facts that are rejected, rather than the frame. In the words of Walter Lippmann (1921), 'We define first, and then see.'

Strategic frame analysis is a tool designed to help us understand the dominant frames that exist in public discourse on an issue. It does this by examining the communications of the media, government, non-governmental organisations, and the public within that frame, and exploring how those dominant frames affect public opinion and choices.

Based on this understanding, it can be decided whether a cause is best served by repeating or breaking those dominant frames of discourse, or by reframing an issue – using different concepts, language and images – to evoke a different way of thinking, facilitating alternative choices. Neurologically, reframing requires a 'rewiring' of the brain which, as a result of repetition over time, results in the frames becoming entrenched in the synapses of people's brains (Lakoff 2003). A key aspect of reframing an issue is to start any communications on an issue in terms of values, rather than of policies or even references to the issue area involved (such as 'the environment').

In the United States, the political right has adopted this approach with some success – designing political communications to resonate with the frames or values of key groups in society, rather than simply promoting 'rational' arguments (Patent and Lakoff 2004).

Developing an over-arching brand

For long-running communications efforts that involve multiple changes in behaviour, campaigns need to promote a hierarchy of messages, rather than a very general message alone. Hence, an overriding message under a powerful brand is followed by specific sub-messages, as, for example, with the UK's 'Think!' road safety campaign, whose messages appeal to people to wear seat belts and not to drink and drive, under a general banner of 'road-safety awareness' (Collins *et al* 2003).

A brand is not just a logo – it is an organising principle for communications that will involve a name or phrase, a tone of voice, and a visual identity, all of which must have emotional appeal. Under this principle, a family of communications activities can take place and, if sustained over time, become instantly recognisable (Calder 2005).

Brands can be a powerful means of shaping consumer behaviour. Once brands are well known and trusted, they can help consumers take quick shortcuts without having to think. They can convey predictability, consistency, performance, and value for money, and they can convey messages about who we are at any particular time on within a given context (Gordon 2002).

These kinds of associations are built up through direct and indirect messaging used by the brand. What a brand says is distinct from how it says it. The latter can be even more influential than the former because it transmits powerful sensory and emotional cues, involving colours, symbols, shapes, textures and images, which people can interpret, rather than just 'rational' cues (ibid).

Using appropriate messengers

Another important element in designing effective communications campaigns is identifying and using messengers and communication channels that connect and resonate most with the target audience, by asking who target audiences respect, listen to or learn most from, and what they read, watch or listen to.

Some people are happy to comply with authority, while others instinctively distrust it or react against it if they think they are being persuaded to do something. Generally, traditional sources of authority are trusted less today than they were in the past. Yet people do need to feel that they can trust an information provider before they accept any information offered.

As we have seen earlier in this chapter, evidence suggests that people trust those with whom they have personal contact or those who exhibit an independence from traditional authority (Cooke 2003). Hence, one solution may be to strengthen the independence of important sources of public information, by creating independent agencies with perceived legitimacy, impartiality and expertise (Steadman 2005).

Another option is to pursue co-branding with trusted sources. Government can leverage its investment in communications by working in partnership with other organisations, including businesses, non-governmental organisations, media outlets and community groups that have a shared interest. This should increase public trust in messages from government, as well as showing the high level of societal consensus that exists for action on the problem and increase the reach of campaign messages and target specific audiences (Calder 2005).

The use of influential role models may also be particularly important given how much learning takes place as a result of social modelling. For some parts of the population – particularly those who have low motivation and ability to engage with an issue – associating a celebrity with a particular behaviour will act as a 'persuasion cue', in a process known as 'peripheral processing', which suggests that there are possible rewards associated with the behaviour in question (Jackson 2005).

Well-known brands could also be persuaded to carry messages. For example, when the solar energy company Solar Century provided solar cells for the reality television show 'Big Brother' house, this helped brand solar power as innovative, modern, fun, and brought it to the homes of the general public (Gordon 2002).

There is also evidence to suggest that people think it would be more appropriate for 'small' lifestyle messages to come from the media, charities or local government, with central government focusing on 'big' messages (OLR 2005a).

Using appropriate communications channels

It is often most effective to offer information in a place and time in which the audience is already thinking about the issue in question. For example, with attempts to influence purchasing decisions, people would prefer more information at the place and time of purchase, through product labelling and 'with product' information, involving some form of scoring or ranking system (Steadman 2005). But on-site information needs to be supplemented by continuous campaigns to influence the years of planning that often shape the larger decisions people take, such as those that involve expensive, non-impulse purchases.

The use of paid, mainstream advertising in broadcast media and print is not considered the most cost-effective means of communicating educational messages to the public (Futerra 2005a). But its role should be reconsidered – not only because it can reach a large proportion of the population, but also, importantly, because it can assign national importance and credibility to an issue in a way that local or community-based initiatives cannot.

Even so, television advertising will not be effective on its own – particularly in today's information-overloaded world, in which people have become adept at screening out messages. Communications need to be more creative and make use of a multitude of potential message placement channels, from websites to product packaging, shopping bags, bills, supermarket promotions, product placement in soap operas and music videos, event sponsorship and schools.

Ultimately, when giving advice, person-to-person engagement is more motivating than information provided impersonally (Steadman 2005). This can be provided through door-stepping or roadshows. And in complex areas where generic information is insufficient, or where consumer engagement is low, interactive advice services may be the most effective means of providing information. These can tailor information to individual consumer circumstances, and are able to resolve difficulties that consumers may have with understanding or applying information.

Communications campaigns that involve promoting new products also need to ensure that marketing chains continue further downstream, with sales teams trained to understand and explain the benefits of new technology (UNEP 2005a).

Repetition, longevity and consistency

Three other critical components of any effective communications campaign – particularly where cultural shifts are required – are the need to ensure that:

- messages are communicated consistently
- key messages are repeated frequently
- the campaign is long-lasting.

For example, the UK Government's drink-driving campaign has succeeded because it has been sustained and reinforced over decades (Collins *et al* 2003). Similarly, behaviour towards wearing seat belts has changed as a result of a 20-year communications campaign, combined with supportive legislation (Calder 2005).

Frequent repetition of a message is particularly important. Ideas become accepted as 'common sense' when words expressing those ideas are repeated sufficiently often that they become the normal way to talk about the issue. When words are repeated, the corresponding frames are evoked repeatedly, and if this happens often enough, they become entrenched in people's brains, like images burnt into a screen (Patent and Lakoff 2004). So, people need to hear or see the message as often, and from as many sources, as possible: in a newspaper, on television, from a neighbour, friend or child, on the internet or on a postcard in the mail (Fenton Communications 2001).

Achieving this, and sustaining communications campaigns over long periods of time, requires long-term commitment and substantial financial investment. The Climate Change Communications Project (established by non-governmental campaigners to design a national climate change campaign) estimated that the core costs of running an effective campaign on climate change in the UK to reach audiences nationwide would be approximately £8 million per annum (Calder 2005).

But if contradictory messages and concepts from significant players persist, any persuasion campaign will be seriously undermined. This means that government needs to maintain a consistent message towards the issue, across departments, and must exemplify the behaviour change it wishes to see. Evidence suggests that people mistrust and ignore exhortations to behave environmentally if they appear inconsistent with policy measures coming from elsewhere in government, or are seen to be at odds with the behaviour of government. That is why it is essential that governments lead by example (Jackson 2005).

The need for consistency also requires that concerted efforts are made to encourage the mainstream media to disseminate supportive messages and concepts – no easy task when there are so many players involved – and to closely examine policy regulating commercial advertising.

Conclusions

The way people do things can seem fixed and immutable, only to change completely in the space of a few years, resulting in a whole new definition of what is 'acceptable' or 'normal'. We now know much more about how such change can be achieved. Critical to a successful approach is the deployment of interventions such as those outlined in this chapter. Successful interventions work with, or on, the main internal and external drivers of behaviour identified in Chapter 8 of this report.

In the most obvious instance, we know that people need to be provided with alternatives that are convenient and affordable, because a strong internal influence on behaviour – people's personal capacity to act – is often constrained by the amount of free time and money they have.

We also know that alternatives must be made to at least appear affordable, by providing ways of spreading any upfront costs over time. This is because of the mental shortcuts that people take, which mean that they are affected more by losses than gains, and discount the future and any delayed benefits from change.

Asking people to make public commitments to change, and deploying prompts to remind them to do so, can help affect the major influence that habit has on behaviours by raising habitual behaviours to people's consciousness.

Publicly-made commitments (or, in a more extreme way, formal contracts) can also increase people's sense of responsibility for changing their behaviour. And giving people feedback on attempts to change behaviour, providing face-to-face engagement, and involving them in group-level change can increase people's sense of agency, as they see and evaluate the impact of their efforts and are given direct, personal support to change.

A sense of agency from group-based engagement can be deepened by drawing people into participatory problem solving. This approach has taken off in the health field, where a new generation of interventions is aimed at changing behaviour through greater patient participation in the delivery of services.

Once alternatives, awareness of a behaviour, and a sense of responsibility and agency to change it are in place, giving people incentives or rewards to actually change can work, as people respond to positive reinforcements (as they also do to negative ones, when penalties are applied).

Probably even more influential is what others are doing around us. Interventions to exemplify change in those whom people look up to, in the workplace and in the community, can all help create new social norms that can have a significant impact on individual behaviour.

Another element of effective behaviour change is communication. The evidence is that communication alone will not change behaviour, but that it can play a role in complementing and reinforcing other interventions.

Given many people's lack of personal capacity (time) to work behaviour changes out themselves, and the need to increase people's sense of responsibility and agency to act, there is a strong case for linking communication to specific behaviour changes, spelling out what people can do, how, why, where and when.

The history of commercial marketing points to a pre-condition for effective communications for behaviour change – know and segment your audience, not only along socio-economic lines, but also by psychological motivations. This is important because we know that a key internal influence on behaviour is people's drive to meet different psychological needs. The most appropriate communications approaches, involving specific messages, messengers, and communications channels, can then be identified accordingly.

Given what we know about the role of emotion, status seeking and the construction of identity in behaviour, effective communications also need to have personal, emotional appeal, and must make behaviour changes appear aspirational. The same could be said for the alternative behaviours themselves.

Communications approaches also need to be designed in ways that take account of the mental shortcuts or frames that people use to make sense of incoming information and accept or reject it, and that shape how they react. Concepts, language and images need to be chosen accordingly. In addition, repetition, staying power and, above all, consistency can make the difference between a successful and unsuccessful campaign.

The challenge for government and others seeking to change the behaviour of the public is to recognise and embrace this full range of psychosocial approaches. Conventional policies are still important – but using the traditional policy palette alone to stimulate climate-friendly behaviour has not worked. We need a new, and broader, approach.

This is a challenge that some parts of government accept: DEFRA, for example, is developing a new strategy for environmental behaviours that if implemented would involve deploying some of the approaches highlighted in this chapter – notably the use of social marketing (DEFRA 2006h). It needs to be supported, acted on and built on in the ways suggested in the following, final chapter.

10. Recommendations: a new approach to stimulating climate-friendly behaviour

The Government has correctly identified behaviour change as an essential element of meeting the climate challenge. Behaviour change is not an easy option. It does not come about by exhortation – particularly when alternatives do not exist, or are invisible, expensive or inconvenient – and it does not represent a get-out clause for governments seeking to avoid taking action.

Many members of the public are concerned about climate change, but they need to be enabled to do more about it – not in an abstract sense, but within the context of the reality of their daily lives, starting from where they are at, rather than where we might like them to be. Unless that happens, inaction is guaranteed.

Until now, a limited number of traditional tools have been used, in a limited and patchy way, and the evidence is that on the whole, this approach has not worked to the extent necessary. Getting people to change climate-related behaviours requires an approach that is based on a deeper understanding of what actually shapes behaviour. That means confronting an array of deep-seated issues that only a systematic and strategic approach can achieve.

A new framework for climate-friendly behaviour

In this report, we propose a new framework to promote climate-friendly behaviour among the public. There are four essential elements to such an approach:

- Prioritising the areas in which behaviour needs to change
- Identifying the key barriers in the priority areas, and which groups of people are particularly involved
- Developing the most appropriate interventions to overcome those barriers
- Developing smart and effective communications.

Each of these is explained below.

Element 1: Prioritising the areas in which behaviour needs to change

A wide range of everyday behaviours contribute to climate change, and the types of behaviour change that will reduce emissions from those activities vary just as widely, as Chapter 1 of this report shows. To have the most effective impact, and avoid a situation where policy is trying to engage on a huge and arbitrary range of behaviours simultaneously, clear criteria need to be used as a basis for initially focusing on a limited number of the most important areas for change.

Element 2: Identifying the key barriers in the priority areas, and which groups of people are particularly involved

The next step in a systematic and strategic approach is to identify the key barriers (both internal and external) to behaviour change in the priority areas. Chapters 3, 4, 5 and 8 of this report show that in domestic energy, road transport and aviation these range widely, from the financial and informational, to the social and psychological. Each area needs to be addressed.

A systematic and strategic approach would also identify which barriers are most significant for different groups – segmented not only by socio-economic criteria, but also using the psychometric groupings employed in modern marketing described in Chapter 9 of this report. This is important for developing communications as a driver for change, and is discussed further below.

Element 3: Developing the most appropriate interventions to overcome those barriers

Having identified the most important areas of behaviour change, and the key potential barriers, the third step is to devise appropriate interventions for different groups of people. To be effective, these should include interventions that will affect the whole range of influences on behaviour. Government has tended to rely on traditional interventions – providing information, influencing prices through taxes and subsidy, and regulation – to try to change behaviour.

These interventions – based on the assumption that individuals are largely rational decision-makers – have a mixed record, and so far have not been successful in bringing the scale of behaviour change required. This is partly because they have not been applied fully and systematically. However, it is also because so far, climate policy has not deployed the full range of psychosocial tools described in Chapter 9. These move beyond the 'rational actor' model of behaviour change, and use a range of techniques that draw on insights from the psychology and sociology of behaviour change.

Interestingly, government is experimenting with some of these approaches in other policy areas that are best approached through behaviour change, such as with chronic health problems, offering a taste of the exciting possibilities that could be developed for stimulating climate-friendly behaviour.

Element 4: Developing smart and effective communications

The intervention that cuts across all areas of behaviour change is communication. Communications can play an important role in supporting other interventions to drive specific, targeted changes in behaviour. They can help stimulate the interest and intention to do things differently, provide the information and guidance for people to do so, and increase the acceptance of policies to encourage pro-climate behaviours.

In the past, government and NGO communications campaigns aiming to motivate people to change their behaviour in climate-friendly ways have failed to engage people effectively, as described in Chapters 4 and 7 of this report. A systematic and strategic approach to communications must involve a thorough research and development phase that involves the public at its heart, to establish: what should be communicated; on what basis; how this should be done; to whom; using which messengers; and through what channels. Government must also take steps to ensure that its actions are consistent with its communications.

Applying the framework

This report recommends that this framework be applied, to develop a more strategic and systematic approach to changing individual behaviour on climate change. It is an approach that parts of government broadly accept – for example, DEFRA has very recently concluded a process that makes some progress towards taking the first two steps set out in the framework described above (DEFRA 2006h).

The challenge now is to apply the framework in order to design effective interventions. To illustrate how this could be done, we propose our own suggestions, based on the research in this report. As the second element of the framework (on barriers) has already been covered in depth in Chapter 5, here we focus on the first, third and fourth elements of the framework:

- Deciding which are the most important behaviours to change
- Developing interventions to overcome the barriers involved
- Developing smart and effective communications.

These steps are described below.

Step 1: Deciding which are the most important behaviours to change

The first step is to develop criteria for prioritising behaviours. The most obvious criterion is the contribution that the behaviour makes to carbon emissions.

In Chapter 1 of this report, the analysis of emissions arising from the activities of individuals shows that the most carbon-heavy behaviours are:

- heating homes (the source of 33 per cent of an average UK individual's emissions)

- car use (29 per cent)
- heating water (12 per cent).

Together, these three behaviours account for almost 75 per cent of all the measurable emissions from individuals. Achieving behaviour change in these three areas would have a major impact.

These form the main focus, but flying is also important. This is because, while smaller in terms of emissions today, its climatic impact is greater than ground-based sources, and it is the most rapidly growing source of emissions. The number of people flying abroad from the UK has risen by 65 per cent in the past ten years, while the number flying domestically is up 70 per cent over the same period. Without major behaviour change, within the next few years flying will become a much larger part of the problem than it is already.

Ultimately, it is hard to avoid the conclusion that the key areas of behaviour to target are domestic heating and hot water, car use and flying. This would mean working to bring about a range of behaviour changes.

Domestic heating and hot water are considered together, because they are closely related, and typically co-produced through a single boiler. As outlined in Chapter 1, the key behaviour changes needed in this area are:

- fitting insulation (wall, loft, hot-water tank and piping, draught-proofing)
- fitting more efficient (condensing) boilers
- switching fuels away from oil and fossil fuel-derived electricity to gas or, better still, away from all fossil fuels to renewable sources of energy, such as solar thermal, biomass, and ground- and air-source heat pumps.

With car use, key changes to reduce emissions include:
- switching to public transport, walking or cycling
- buying more fuel-efficient cars
- using alternative fuels.

With flying, the main options are to:
- make fewer flights
- switch modes of travel (to train, coach or boat), which is likely to mean taking holidays nearer to home
- offset emissions.

These changes in behaviour represent varying degrees of difficulty. Governments will naturally want to consider which behaviours are likely to be easiest to change when determining priorities. In the past, this criterion has been used to target very small-scale behaviour changes that cost the individual and government very little, but that have only a modest impact on emissions.

Cost, while clearly an important consideration, is just one of a host of potential barriers to behaviour change that need to be considered when deciding which behaviours would be easiest and most effective to target.

Other factors need to be considered too. Influencing one-off behaviours is easier than effecting a lasting change in routine behaviour. Also, those kinds of behaviours that have a higher social status are likely to be easier to persuade people to adopt than lower-status ones. Combined with the need to target behaviours that have the most impact on emissions, this might lead to focusing on the installation of some micro-renewables, and driving low-carbon cars, including hybrids. Unlike other changes (such as fitting insulation or taking a bus), changes such as driving a hybrid or investing in solar PV have a status aspect, exciting the interest and aspirations of other people.

Installing microgeneration technologies has the added advantage of being the most likely to catalyse other climate-friendly behaviours. Evidence suggests that installing micro-renewables can stimulate a greater awareness of, and interest in, energy use in the home and while driving, catalysing improvements in energy efficiency in the home and even, in some cases, lower-carbon transport choices (SDC/NCC 2005). So there is a strong case to include investment in micro-electricity-producing renewables (such as micro-wind and solar photovoltaics) as part of the strategy.

Step 2: Choosing appropriate interventions for these areas

With each of the priority areas identified above, governments will seek to maximise the use of interventions that do not require behaviour change at all – by, for example, regulating to increase energy or emissions standards for appliances, houses and cars, or by introducing renewables obligations or upstream cap-and-trade schemes for electricity and fuel suppliers.

But this will still leave a large proportion of the problem in the hands of the individual, who needs to actively choose to behave differently. In this respect, government is already applying a range of measures to try to change behaviour in the areas that we have identified as priorities, as discussed in Chapter 7 of this report. However, in most cases, these measures have not been sufficient to produce a step change in behaviour and emissions.

This is partly because where measures are appropriate, they have been too weak. But it is also because government has not been systematic in engaging with the full range of influences that have been identified in the sociological and psychological literature, and overcoming barriers accordingly.

As we saw in Chapter 8, the factors that shape the behaviour of individuals do not just include traditional socio-economic ones such as wealth, age, and where people are in their life cycle. They also include a series of other internal influences on behaviour, such as psychological motivation, status seeking, identity shaping, habits, mental shortcuts and a sense of agency, as well as a series of external influences, such as the behaviour of others around us, societal norms, the directness of experiences, and rewards and penalties. These factors lead us to the need to use a wider range of interventions, as discussed in Chapter 9.

How the interventions might be applied

This section offers some examples of how the types of interventions described in Chapter 9 of this report might be applied in parallel with more traditional approaches, in each of the priority areas listed on p156. It provides a range of possible options for government to consider, and it is not intended to set out a comprehensive list or road-map. Policymakers would need to cost them, sequence them carefully, and in some cases, trial them before implementing them on a national scale.

The specific proposals are detailed below, set out within the three areas of particular concern: domestic heating and hot water; car use; and flying.

The proposals are then subdivided into activities within all or some of the following categories:

- raising understanding
- improving image
- social proofing
- setting attractive rewards (and repellent penalties)
- increasing affordability
- ensuring group support
- providing convenience
- committing to change.

Domestic heating and hot water

As explained previously these two categories are taken together because they are closely related and are typically co-produced through a single boiler. Increasing the uptake of insulation, efficient boilers and fuel switching (here we consider both heat and electricity-producing renewables for the reasons stated earlier) involves overcoming a number of practical and psychosocial barriers, set out in Chapter 5 of this report, that need to be overcome.

These include:

- the invisibility of energy use
- inaccurate or poor information about the products involved
- their dull or eccentric image
- off-putting capital costs

- the difficulty in getting the same rewards for micro-renewable solutions as widescale renewable generation
- the sheer hassle and inconvenience involved.

A combination of interventions is needed to overcome these obstacles, as set out below.

Raising understanding

To increase the deployment of energy-reducing measures, interventions are needed to increase the visibility of energy use in people's homes, increase householders' understanding of how to reduce it, and address misconceptions about the cost and viability of the solutions.

As a minimal measure, government should require energy companies to put more information on their customers' bills, allowing customers to compare their energy use over time, with benchmarks, along with the associated carbon impact. However, bills still come only once a quarter (or, for those who pay over the internet, not at all), are often inaccurate due to infrequent meter readings, and can provide only crude feedback. The starting point is to improve the accuracy of bills. Current practice can only be improved if suppliers are required to read meters at least twice a year.

Also needed are 'smarter' meters, which can be read automatically and give information about use over time. Visible consumer displays are also needed, along with well-designed forms of real-time energy feedback. Real-time energy feedback devices can give 'live' information, and can be linked to individual appliances or uses, so that consumers can see the effect of adopting specific energy-saving measures instantly. Their use needs to be moved beyond the pilot stage.

The possibility of a five-year programme to roll out the installation of these devices was raised in the 2006 Energy Review, and this proposal is now out to consultation. The Government should draw up plans to start such a UK-wide programme in 2007 for consumer displays compatible with future smart-metering solutions.

Smart meters are already commercially available, and can give consumers information on energy use over different time periods, from the past hour to the past day, week, month or year. Better metering products are especially needed for gas, which is the main fuel for heating and hot water. Currently, government policy is not to legislate for the rollout of smart metering, but rather to specify technical standards for metering and to look to the market to provide. However, this will not happen unless, and until, the incentives are in place for suppliers or district network operators to do this.

Currently, it is householders, rather than suppliers, who 'own' gas and electricity meters and are responsible for them. This means that utility companies would have to persuade householders to invest money in better devices. This does not fit well with the business model of selling gas and electricity, and of disturbing consumers as little as possible.

One way of changing this situation may be to include the provision of smart meters in the Energy Efficiency Commitment measures, which would give suppliers an incentive to promote these meters with their customers. The Government is currently consulting on this option, and should adopt it. If this fails to stimulate sufficient uptake, the Government should reverse its position on a national rollout of smart meters by energy suppliers – which has been the approach adopted by the Italian government.

However, householders need more than information about their energy use. They also need more specific information about how they can reduce it. Individualised home-energy audits are particularly effective, since they involve face-to-face communication and interaction – which are more powerful motivators of change than self-auditing internet-based initiatives – to tell householders what their property's CO_2 impact is and how they can reduce it.

To some extent, this is already happening. Some energy suppliers are offering householders free energy audits (although they are not particularly widely promoted), and the Home Information Pack Energy Performance Certificate, being introduced in 2007, will mean compulsory energy auditing and labelling (paid for by householders) of all homes being sold or rented out. However, this still leaves many homes that will not be audited.

To go further, the Government should agree a goal of providing each UK home with an energy audit by 2012, and explore ways of providing the necessary resources to expand the energy-audit programme and to train more auditors – possibly through the EST, or a new agency.

The Government should also take steps to correct widespread misconceptions about the costs and payback times of energy-efficiency products and the reliability and suitability of microgeneration technologies. Accurate and authoritative information on these products should be targeted at builders, including through training programmes. The Government should also work with the Micro-Power Council, the Renewable Energy Association and other trade bodies, to explore the establishment of an authoritative micro-renewables accreditation body to set standards and certify the performance of microgeneration technologies, as well as to provide accurate information to the public.

There is currently no national mechanism to provide renewables advice. The Government needs to ensure there is one. It should rationalise and improve advice about micro-renewables to the public and integrate such a service with advice on energy efficiency, under the overall umbrella of 'energy services'. The issue currently falls between DEFRA and DTI but could be combined more rationally within a single agency, such as the Energy Saving Trust (which is piloting such a combined approach in three sustainable-energy centres).

Improving image
While useful, information alone is unlikely to bridge the gap between awareness and action (Oxera 2005). In this sector, one of the obstacles to overcome on the path towards greater public action is the image of the measures involved.

Condensing boilers and insulation are of no intrinsic or aesthetic interest: to most they appear dull, and will generally be sacrificed to other home improvements where possible. Even more expensive renewable heat technologies, such as ground-source heat pumps and biomass boilers, are unlikely to have huge status either. One way of dealing with this problem is to roll all of these measures into a wider 'green home' package that has aspirational appeal.

Companies outside the energy sector could develop 'green home makeover' services, as part of the wider hand-holding service described in 'Providing convenience' below, to remove hassle and time costs. DEFRA is currently supporting a trial in London along these lines (see Box 10.1), and it should continue to support this approach with incubation money.

For the substantial group of people motivated by seeking status (see Chapter 9 of this report), the example of celebrities endorsing and taking action on domestic energy may also help improve the image of related measures and spur people to act in the same way as the celebrity. Steps should be taken to proactively build up celebrity support in this area, to rival that for Prius cars.

The 'alternative' image of micro-renewables such as micro-wind turbines may be off-putting to the more risk averse and the more consumer oriented. This can partly be changed by steps to normalise their use (described further below). But it could also be altered by a greater emphasis on better design. The majority of micro-renewable technologies on sale have clearly been designed by engineers, not product designers. Government could act here by setting up aesthetic design competitions for micro-renewables – an approach that could be extended to real-time energy-feedback devices and even traditional products that are hard to sell, such as external wall insulation.

Social proofing
Given how much people are influenced by the behaviour of others and dominant social norms (see Chapter 8 of this report), further steps are needed to normalise measures to reduce emissions in this sector, beyond recruiting celebrities, so that the 'social proof' about how to behave can be seen all around us.

One way to do this is for government to increase support for community or group-level initiatives (see 'Ensuring group support' below) so that people feel that 'people like them', their neighbours or work colleagues, and local people they look up to, such as professionals they meet, are adopting these behaviours too.

Government leadership through action could also be a powerful factor. Some central government departments now source 'green' tariff electricity, but only one has micro-renewables on site. This needs to change. Every government department should be set a target to source 10 per cent of its energy from on-site renewables by 2010. Some city governments are already promoting flagship projects, including London, where PV panels are to be fitted to City Hall, and the building that houses the Regional Development Agency has a mixed PV and micro-wind system. All other major cities should follow London's lead.

However, government has wider opportunities to show leadership. For example, a major school rebuilding programme is underway. 'Schools for the Future' aims to rebuild or renew every secondary school in the country in the next 10–15 years, and £2.2 billion was made available for 2005/06. Currently, the Government is providing guidance on sustainable design for schools in this programme, but in most cases there are no measures in place to ensure that on-site renewables form part of the design package. There is a massive educational and social-proofing opportunity here – much more important than the actual power generated. And the amount of micro-renewable capacity, and the additional cost of ensuring the inclusion of micro-renewables, could be small relative to the cost of the entire programme.

Hence, government should explore ways of providing the funding necessary for every school to have an appropriate form of on-site renewable-energy generation by 2015, with local authorities and schools deciding which technology to opt for. The Government should extend this approach to other public buildings, such as those managed by health trusts, by expanding and ringfencing funding for civic leadership through the Low Carbon Buildings Programme.

Setting attractive rewards

Another option to motivate behaviour change in this area is to offer some form of reward. For large-scale energy-reducing measures, this could be a simple cash incentive, which has been effective in motivating domestic energy-efficiency investments in the Canadian EnerGuide for Homes programme. In the UK, British Gas has experimented with £100 council tax rebates as an incentive, with some success, and has subsequently rolled this scheme out to almost 1 million households in 16 local authorities, with a further 40 councils across the country expressing interest (DEFRA 2006b). Central government has not mandated this approach, but could – and should explore ways of doing so.

'Feed-in tariffs' to stimulate the market in micro-renewables are another option. In Germany and Spain, PV in particular has grown extremely rapidly because of a guaranteed reward for the electricity generated. In Germany, this policy, combined with grant support, led to an increase in PV generation between 1993 and 1999 of more than 1,000 per cent – some 30 times that seen in the UK over the same period (European Environment Agency 2001). In the UK, until the 2006 Climate Change and Sustainable Energy Act, there was no guarantee that any surplus electricity generated by a household would find a buyer at all. Following the Act, if suppliers do not now offer a feed-in tariff, the Government has the power to force them to do so, and it should use that power.

However, prices offered by suppliers will continue to be lower than prices paid for electricity by households. This will only change if government legislates for a specified feed-in tariff, as has been the case in Germany and Spain. The UK government should adopt this approach, specifying what the level of the tariff should be, and over what period. Once the upfront cost of micro-renewable technologies falls sufficiently, this policy could be phased out.

Another approach is to allow householders investing in microgeneration to claim 100 per cent enhanced capital allowances against tax, in the same way that companies investing in power stations can. Research suggests that this would have an impact on payback times equivalent to a guaranteed export reward, but the gain would come in the first year (Watson *et al* 2006).

Given what we know about people's tendency to place greater weight on avoiding negative experiences than seeking positive ones, and their tendency to discount the future (see Chapter 8 of this report), this could be an even more effective measure than guaranteed feed-in tariffs. Hence, the Government should simultaneously examine the possibility of adopting this approach, and, as with feed-in tariffs, if adopted phase it out once the upfront cost of micro-renewable technologies falls sufficiently.

Increasing affordability
While misperceptions about the costs of cavity-wall or loft insulation can be tackled through the home-energy audit and advice programmes described above, some measures – especially the installation of condensing boilers (which is now mandatory), domestic combined heat and power (CHP), renewable heat technologies and solid wall insulation – do have a relatively high capital cost. Some renewable electricity-producing renewables have even higher ones. The evidence shows that people discount the future heavily, and so upfront costs obscure longer-term paybacks.

The way that costs and rewards are perceived may mean that policies impacting on headline price are more effective than policies that impact on payback times. One way to address this problem is to lower capital costs.

Another is to convert capital costs into a stream of payments.

The Government is currently pursuing the first of these options, by offering reduced VAT on energy-efficiency and micro-renewable products if installed (an approach that the Government should pursue further, by working with the EU to allow reduced VAT on DIY insulation products). It is also offering subsidy through the Energy Efficiency Commitment, although most of this tends to go on cavity-wall insulation).

The Government also offers a programme of grants for microgeneration, but this needs to be significantly expanded and measures taken to ensure there are no funding gaps in future. A less direct and longer-term way to reduce capital costs would be for the Government to consider mandating on-site renewable generation for all new buildings, thereby increasing production volumes of these technologies and achieving greater economies of scale.

The second option for converting capital costs into a stream of payments could be stimulated by the introduction of an energy-reduction commitment in place of the Energy Efficiency Commitment (EEC). This proposal is currently out for consultation following the 2006 Energy Review. The Government should certainly pursue this option, and should bring its introduction forward to 2008 from the current proposal of 2011. At the very least, EEC3 (running from 2008 to 2011) should be a transition towards it. Energy suppliers are in an ideal position to finance large energy-efficiency investments, as they can offer on-bill repayments of capital cost, which can be set against lower bills than would otherwise be the case.

Government should also create incentives for banks and building societies to offer 'green' mortgages and re-mortgages, so that the capital cost of energy-efficiency work done on a house and microgeneration installation at the point of purchase (or, for existing homeowners, at any point) could be rolled into the mortgage – which is typically much larger. Lower energy bills would mean a higher disposable income against which to borrow.

However, these kinds of arrangements have only tended to emerge where there is a requirement not only to label the energy performance of a home (as in the forthcoming Home Information Pack), but also where minimum energy-performance standards are required at point of sale, as in parts of California.

The Government could provide top-up finance for 'green' loans itself (as it does for small and medium enterprises through the Carbon Trust), but this could be an expensive option. Alternatively, it could take steps to increase the demand for such a service, either by increasing the number of voluntary commitments that people make to increase the energy performance of their homes (see below), or by making it mandatory at the point of sale through regulation, as in California.

The Government could thereby potentially achieve major behavioural change in the owner-occupied sector. With a turnover in ownership of 7.5 per cent a year, and allowing for the fact that some homes change hands frequently while others do not, a large proportion of the sector could be brought up to a minimum energy performance within 20 years (DCLG 2006a).

Ensuring group support
Even if people had better information about their energy use, how to reduce it, the rewards for doing so, and schemes to reduce the size of any upfront costs, they still need help in actually delivering the changes concerned.

One way of doing this is through local- or community-level mutual support groups, such as Global Action Plan's 'eco-teams'. As described in Chapter 9 of this report, members of such groups set themselves goals and measure their progress (for example, by monitoring their use of energy in domestic heating, which is easily verifiable). They also meet regularly to share their experience, feedback, praise and knowledge on how to do more. Such an approach can strongly increase individuals' sense of agency and resolve necessary to carry out the desired changes.

The other possibility that such groups open up is a community approach to renewable energy, beyond individual investments in micro-renewables. In the UK, this is currently confined to a handful of small wind-farm projects, but, as the experience of Germany shows, involvement in community climate-friendly energy projects can have a powerful appeal.

Government should significantly expand its financial support for such groups so that within five years most households have access to a local group, and so that greater demand can be stimulated for their use – particularly among those who are less advantaged and proactive. Government should also set up an agency to provide such groups with technical advice – particularly to ensure successful initiatives are replicated. Local government can play a role here too, by initiating such groups as part of their Local Agenda 21 programmes.

Providing convenience
For many, even if group support were available, a major barrier to reducing emissions from heating and hot water would still exist: the hassle of organising insulation, a new boiler or a microgeneration system in the home, and the intrusion of installers. This is especially the case for those in the mid-life cycle, who are often short of time, or for the elderly, who can feel particularly vulnerable to strangers in their home. A key intervention here is to make behaviour change convenient and safe.

Government could help achieve this by supporting the development of a hand-holding project-management service that takes away the hassle and the risk from householders. With this approach, an organisation links people up with a dedicated personal account manager who will:

- organise a site survey on the person's behalf
- provide accurate and up-to-date information on technology choices
- pre-select and screen any contractors for quality and security
- project manage the work, including overseeing and checking on the quality of the work (they might even have a house key so that the work can be carried out while the householder is at work)
- follow up on any concerns that the householder may have.

This type of service is grouped under the 'lifestyle management' or 'new concierge' sector. At present, these services can be expensive, aimed at those who are cash-rich but time-poor. However, their aim is purely to remove the hassle and risk relating to installing technology, managing contractors, and so on, and they do overcome those barriers.

The current Energy Efficiency Commitment programme does this only minimally, and does not have quality of service as its prime objective. It is possible that the conversion of the EEC programme into an energy-reduction commitment (see p164) might act as an incentive for energy-supply companies to develop such services on a competitive basis. The sooner such a commitment could be introduced the better (see p164), otherwise alternative measures to increase such offerings will be needed.

Committing to change
Even if the necessary behaviour changes can be made to appear as attractive, affordable and convenient as possible, by implementing all the measures described above, further steps are needed to encourage people to actually commit to action.

One way to do this would be for government to explore the option of forcing a degree of action, by requiring that UK homes at the point of sale (and possibly even rental) meet minimum energy-performance standards. The Government's new Energy Performance Certificate, as part of the Home Information Pack, could be the first step towards such an approach, but it needs to overcome resistance from estate agents and some house sellers, and even if the scheme is implemented it would still leave many homes unaffected.

An alternative or complementary approach would be to use the energy-auditing process described above to commit people to action on a voluntary basis. Once the auditors had completed their survey and recommendations for action (through the Energy Performance Certificate process, the Energy Efficiency Commitment or an expanded government-funded home-energy auditing programme as recommended above), they could ask

Box 10.1: Green Homes Service trial

In 2005, the London Climate Change Agency and the Design Council undertook a project to see how principles of product and service design could be applied to home-energy issues – particularly with a view to discovering whether the principles of desirability, convenience and aesthetics could be brought to the fore.

This work, partly inspired by the example of EnerGuide for Homes in Canada, was supported by a grant from the Energy Saving Trust, which also funded the subsequent development of a business plan for a pilot of a new kind of domestic-energy service. This service incorporates many of the ideas explored in this report. It looks at energy use in the home but also at other potentially 'green' issues, including waste and water. In contrast to the Energy Efficiency Commitment approach, it looks at the energy performance of the whole house, offering a survey with a pressure test to assess air-tightness.

In Canada, this approach has worked as a major motivator of householder investment because it demonstrates so dramatically the waste of energy in a home. The Green Homes Energy Service offers both traditional energy-efficiency products and micro-renewables.

Perhaps most importantly, the emphasis is on service. The pilot is being developed with a 'new concierge' company, with a client manager assigned to each account. For those who want it, handholding is offered all the way through the process of installing energy-efficiency products or microgeneration, with Green Homes Service staff project managing the work, which is carried out by pre-accredited contractors. Finally, there is a reward in the form of an incentive payment, and also the possibility of trialling finance from a green mortgage to cover some of the costs of products installed.

The Green Homes Service pilot is being supported by the Mayor of London, DEFRA, and the London Development Agency. Trials began on a small scale in Lewisham in late 2006 and early 2007 to test proof the concept. If successful, a larger-scale pilot will be rolled out over the course of 2007.

---

householders to sign a written voluntary commitment to implement some or all of the recommendations made.

Evidence suggests that this would increase the chances of action being taken (see Chapter 9 of this report). The auditors could then provide householders with information about how to install the relevant measures, including financing options, support groups and, in time, 'green home' service companies.

Car use
Attempts to reduce emissions from car use by switching to public transport,

walking or cycling, or by buying more fuel-efficient or alternatively fuelled cars face several deep-seated psychosocial and practical barriers (see Chapter 5 of this report). These include:

- the greater convenience, status, identity shaping and emotional role of cars compared to public transport, cycling or walking
- habit
- misperceptions about relative costs and convenience of alternatives
- poor facilities and infrastructure for alternatives
- the higher costs of alternatively-powered cars.

A combination of interventions is needed to overcome these obstacles.

Overall, driving is an area in which psychosocial factors bear particularly heavily on behaviour. Evidence shows that successful interventions based on this insight are being tried in many locations across the UK and Europe (Sloman 2006). These use a combination of marketing, better information, and small practical changes to alternatives to the car – often about improving ease or comfort. Good practice already exists. The challenge for government is to understand it and support its rollout nationally.

Surveys show that cars are only really necessary for about 20 per cent of journeys. For a further 40 per cent of journeys, an alternative is possible but inconvenient. For the final 40 per cent, cars are being used only because there is a misperception that they are easier or cheaper (Sloman 2006). That means that up to 80 per cent of journeys made by car could be avoided if the right interventions are made. Clearly, not all drivers will be easily shifted from their cars. However, up to half (including people who feel guilty about their car use and those who aspire to be more climate-friendly) could be (Anable 2005 cited in Sloman 2006).

Providing convenience
In any effort to encourage the public to switch from car use to public transport or cycling, a critical component is to improve the convenience of these alternatives. For the 40 per cent of journeys where alternatives exist but are inadequate, a myriad of changes – including many that are small scale – will be needed to improve the convenience and safety of alternatives.

Many of the policy recommendations made here will require an increase in resources channelled towards cycling and walking, travel planning and, especially, on improvements in public transport. As noted in Chapter 7, while spending on public transport has increased year-on-year over the past decade, much of this has gone on maintaining struggling services rather than actually expanding capacity and improving quality. For example, Britain still lags behind many European, and even Asian, countries in the extent of the high-speed rail network in place (CFIT 2004a). At the same time, funding for investment in road building increased sharply between 2005 and 2006.

For all new transport spending, proposals should be subject to an emissions assessment before funds are released. The Government should make investing in an affordable, high quality and convenient public transport system its priority, aspiring to the levels of service seen in continental Europe.

Bus services have improved, both inside and outside of London. However, central government needs to work with local authorities and bus companies, and increase support to improve services further (CFIT 2004b). On main routes, more frequent buses, and more bus lanes to reduce waiting times and increase bus speeds, are needed. Buses need to be made more comfortable, clean and attractive, and better shelters showing real-time information are required. Government should also reform the Bus Service Operators Grant (a refund on fuel duty paid by bus operators), which acts as a major block to operators buying hybrid or alternative-fuel buses.

One way of improving bus services is to share best practice between bus companies around the country, drawing on the many isolated examples of successful initiatives that have resulted in increased bus use. For example, some bus operators have very successfully marketed specific services at particular groups such as an 'executive' bus with leather seats and extra legroom for commuters, and buses with increased space for baby buggies to encourage people with babies on to bus services. Government should ensure best practice such as this is shared (see below).

Government also needs to take steps to encourage the provision of 'bus taxis'. These taxis, which can be booked in advance but are shared with other people travelling in roughly the same direction, have been highly successful in Holland (Sloman 2006). Thornier to achieve but potentially more significant is the need for action to make train services faster, as well as more frequent and more comfortable.

In relation to cycling, steps should also be taken to ensure the provision of:

- more and better cycling lanes and advanced stop lines
- more and better shower and parking facilities at work and in public places
- cycle hire facilities at train and bus stations
- better systems for transport bicycles on trains.

Measures are also needed to encourage more walking, including by reallocating more road space to pedestrians in towns and cities, and increasing support for programmes to encourage children to walk to school instead of being driven, such as the 'walking bus' initiative in primary schools. Greater provision of car clubs, car-sharing services and remote working should be another objective.

Across all these areas, there are examples of excellent practice in different parts of the UK. If the Government wants a nationwide public transport system that makes climate-friendly transport choices easier and more attractive, it urgently needs to provide a mechanism for sharing these examples, in partnership with the Commission for Integrated Transport. It should therefore fund an independent organisation to establish a forum for sharing best practice in this area. This would be a highly cost-effective intervention.

In the longer term, government needs to build in the requirement for high-density mixed-use development into the planning system at all levels, in order to help create a less car-dependent society. The Barker Review of Land Use Planning focused on removing planning barriers to growth so that Britain can have a planning system fit for a globalised economy. But Britain also needs a climate-friendly planning system, to ensure that economic gains are not undermined. A planning system that promotes unrestrained car use will be self-defeating. Hence, restrictions on out-of-town developments should not be eased. More generally, planning guidance and public spending priorities must favour the development of public transport infrastructure over road networks.

The Government's task is not just to provide more convenient alternatives to the car. It is also to support the more efficient everyday use of cars, by promoting eco-driving techniques. This can be achieved through the driving test curriculum and by promoting the techniques to current licence holders. Companies should also provide employees and staff drivers with eco-driving guidance as part of business travel plans – especially for fleet drivers.

Government also needs to make it convenient for people to use cars powered by alternative, low-carbon fuels. It can do this by creating the infrastructure necessary, for example, for the widespread availability of biofuels to ensure that that biofuel-powered cars (such as the Saab 9–5 BioPower car, which runs on an 85:15 per cent mix of bioethanol and diesel) can be viable. Currently, there are only a handful of fuelling stations in the country. The Energy Saving Trust already runs a DfT-funded programme providing support for alternative refuelling stations and electric recharging points, but this needs to be scaled up to provide nationwide coverage rapidly.

Raising understanding

Another very significant barrier to change in this sector that needs to be overcome is the deeply held view that there is no convenient alternative to car use. Surveys of cities as diverse as Perth in Australia, and Kassel in Germany, show that in some circumstances, there is a good alternative available to using cars, but in many cases people (43 per cent, in the case of Perth) do not know about them (Sloman 2006).

The German marketing company Socialdata has pioneered an approach that has proven able to help change this situation. This approach, known as 'individualised travel marketing', carefully targets tailored information to households about existing alternative travel options (walking, cycling and public transport), including journey times and costs, which meet their individual needs. It also sometimes gives households that have not used public transport recently free tickets, to tempt them to experience it for themselves.

The approach is highly personalised, and is initiated through contact with households on the doorstep and by phone. It usually targets households that are non-regular users of alternatives to the car who are interested in receiving information on alternatives.

The approach has been applied successfully in behaviour-change programmes targeting a total of nearly three million people in Australia, the United States, Canada, Germany, Austria, Switzerland, France, and the UK (where it was introduced with Sustrans, under the TravelSmart programme), leading to significant increases in the use of public transport and declines in car use (Sloman 2006). It has helped inspire the establishment of a personalised travel-planning programme now being rolled out across London. The Government and local authorities should consider committing to, and explore ways of providing the resources necessary for, a national rollout of this approach to all households in urban areas of England over a 10-year period.

Smart travel choice plans are often funded, designed and launched at local-authority level. Greater flexibility in funding, and higher regard for the effectiveness of these measures among policymakers, is needed for them to be more extensively applied. The Government should improve the flexibility of Local Transport Plan funding so that it supports such plans, rather than only funding capital projects (Grayling *et al* 2005). It should also strengthen Planning Guidance Policy 13 on transport, to ensure that planning authorities require travel plans to be drawn up before planning permission is granted to new developments.

Work travel plans and school travel plans have also been shown to be effective at local level (Sloman 2006). The Government has an ambition for all schools to have a travel plan by 2010, and is providing a number of grants to help achieve this target. A parallel approach is needed for business. This could involve setting up an advisory service such as (or through) the Carbon Trust, to advise and assist businesses in preparing travel plans and services.

Habitual drivers need particular help to change. Prompts are needed to remind them to break their habit and use alternatives instead. The Government should run an open competition – including in schools – to design stickers and other prompts for use in the home and car. Winning designs could be distributed free through a range of channels, including supermarkets, newspapers, environmental NGO mailouts and Global Action Plan groups.

Steps are also needed to raise understanding about the comparative contribution that different cars make to climate change so that people can make informed choices. Labelling has a track record of increasing the purchase of environmentally high-performing domestic products, but at present there is only a voluntary scheme, for new cars, and in any case many showrooms do not display the labels on their vehicles. The Government needs to address this by making emissions-related car labelling mandatory for all new car sales as consumers search for a new vehicle. When feasible, the scheme should be extended to second-hand car 'supermarkets' and, more widely, to the dominant second-hand market.

Improving image
The car is the ultimate status symbol, and owning a vehicle offers an important way of expressing personal identity. In this regard, collective forms of travel will be hard pushed to match what the car can offer. But steps can, and certainly should, be taken to improve the woeful status and image of alternatives to the car – notably buses (which are the least aspirational form of transport) and, to a lesser extent, cycling (which has an eccentric image). Steps also need to be taken to improve the image of more fuel-efficient or alternatively powered cars, which can be seen as being embarrassing, low-performing and ugly.

One way to do this is to bring celebrity endorsements to bear, so that public transport and cycling can appear more desirable, providing aspirational role models that will appeal to the people with strong status-seeking needs (see Chapter 9 of this report). To some extent, this already happens for cars like the Toyota Prius, but efforts could be made to step up the number of celebrity endorsements, especially from public figures with high visibility with motorists, such as Premiership footballers and their partners.

Another approach is to encourage better designs for buses, trains and low-carbon cars, to make them more attractive. The Government should organise a competition for aspirational buses and trains, through the Design Council, that involves the major franchisees on rail and bus routes.

A parallel approach is to erode the status and image of conventional cars, with communications focusing on the aspects of car use that the public feel negative about, such as congestion, pollution and injuries from accidents.

At a minimum, there is a need for an advertising code of good practice for cars. The European Commission has announced that, as part of a package of measures to tackle emissions from cars, it will ask companies to sign up to such a code by mid-2007. If this proves slow, the UK Government should move ahead anyway. As with health warnings on tobacco products, all car advertising should carry bold and visible warnings about the contribution of driving to climate change.

> ## Box 10.2: Smart marketing
>
> The town of Aylesbury in Buckinghamshire has shown that bus travel can be made more desirable through a careful mix of design and marketing. The local bus service was advertised on the bus itself, and included the slogan 'Every ten minutes' written in large letters across the back. A glossy leaflet was produced with timetable info, but designed to look like a car advertisement. A letter and brochure was sent to everyone living within five minutes of the route (5,000 people). A follow-up offer was made of a free ticket for anyone who had not yet tried the service, and the buses were parked in the market square for maximum visibility.
>
> Passenger numbers increased by one third in a few weeks. A year later, this figure had increased by 42 per cent.
>
> A similar scheme in Perth, Scotland, managed to achieve a 60 per cent increase in passenger numbers.
>
> Source: Adapted from Sloman 2006

Social proofing

Further steps are needed to normalise behaviours to reduce transport emissions so that new social norms can be created. One way to help do this is for the Government to provide leadership through action. Ministers need to be seen to use low-carbon transport options, and government needs to encourage public-service staff to exemplify sought behaviour changes too.

Ministers and MPs should keep travel diaries, posted on appropriate websites, showing their use of buses, trains, cycling and walking. The prime minister (and, indeed, leaders of all political parties) should stipulate that unless an urgent vote at the House of Commons is involved, all journeys within Whitehall and Westminster should be by bus, on foot or by bicycle.

Other approaches are for Government to increase support for community and local mutual support groups so that people feel that 'people like them' are adopting these new behaviours too (see above), and for employers to encourage low-carbon travel plans among employees so that the desired behaviours are also in evidence among work colleagues.

Setting attractive rewards and repellent penalties

Approaches aimed at changing the psychology of travel choices need to be aligned with measures that offer people rewards for adopting new behaviours and penalties for pursuing business as usual. It is important that these influence the relative costs involved – especially since the declining trend in the cost of car travel contrasts with that of public transport.

As a first step, VED incentives need to be improved for fuel-efficient vehicles, and disincentives increased for less efficient vehicles, introducing an escalator for the higher bands and freezing or further reducing the lower bands. Consumer research shows that 75 per cent of new car buyers would only swap bands if there were differentials of £300 or more between bands (DfT 2003a). Government should aim to achieve this level over time, getting there in increments, with an annual rise of £50 in the differential between each band.

The Government should explore the possibility of using revenues from the higher-band VED charges to restore its programme of technology-neutral subsidies for those buying low-carbon vehicles, for five years, to replace the PowerShift programme, which ended in 2005.

Another effective approach in helping drive behaviour change is to make people pay for services as they are consumed. This tends to draw attention to cost, which is currently not the case with car use. Road pricing could hence play a very useful role. The Secretary of State for Transport has made advancing the debate on road pricing a personal priority, but a detailed scheme design has yet to be decided.

An important consideration will be what happens to existing motoring taxes. Research by ippr showed that if revenue raised through road pricing is offset by cuts in fuel duty (making the scheme revenue neutral overall), the result will be an increase in CO_2 emissions from road transport. Conversely, a revenue-raising scheme that levied road-pricing charges in addition to existing taxes would produce a decrease in emissions (Grayling et al 2004). If on the other hand cuts are made to Vehicle Excise Duty, it will be necessary to impose a similar emissions-based banding system on the road-pricing scheme to ensure that incentives to buy and use more fuel-efficient vehicles are not lost.

If such an emissions-based banding system were imposed on a road-pricing scheme, it could act as a powerful incentive. Hybrid cars are exempt from the London Congestion Charge, and analysis shows that this has provided a very strong incentive to buy them, as a result of people seeking to avoid paying an additional tax rather than a rational economic decision.

However, public attitudes still remain a key barrier to the introduction of a national road-pricing scheme (Bird and Morris 2006). To help overcome opposition, any scheme must be accompanied by investments in public transport, as was the case with the largely successful Congestion Charge in London.

In addition, further workplace policies are needed, to encourage the use of public transport and cycling. Work travel plans are increasingly effective for workplaces in city centres, but those located at the edge of cities, or on industrial parks, face bigger problems. The Government should examine the option of subsidising employers to encourage the provision of shuttle buses for staff – possibly financed by an increase in company car tax for high CO₂ emission bands.

Increasing affordability
Further measures are needed to reduce the current premium on low-carbon cars which, for a model such as the Prius, can amount to paying £4,000–5,000 more than for a conventionally fuelled vehicle (see Chapter 5 of this report).

In addition to the subsidy programme described above, the Government should find ways of supporting finance packages for low-carbon cars, through a topping-up provision, phasing out over five years as the market matured, similar to the proposed support for green mortgages (see above).

The substantial purchasing power of public-sector procurement needs to be deployed too, to bring down prices. Purchasing low-carbon cars in appropriate public-sector fields would contribute to stimulating the market, and would set an appropriate example to industry and the public.

Until the spring of 2006, the Government had a target for at least 10 per cent of its fleet cars to be low carbon. Since then, a new target has been adopted, based on emissions rather than technologies, to reduce CO₂ from road vehicles used for Government administrative operations by 15 per cent by 2010/2011, relative to 2005/2006 levels.

However, the really big opportunities exist elsewhere in the public sector – especially across local authorities (including public transport franchises), health trusts and emergency services. The Government should make available additional funding to those bodies that adopt a target at least as ambitious as that of central government, in order to help them meet this target through a mixture of demand management and procurement of low-carbon vehicles.

Committing to change
A final approach is to reinforce people's intention to change their travel behaviours and promote a greater sense of responsibility for doing so, by asking them to make a commitment to change.

Group commitments may work well in this context, since groups enable people to check on each other and encourage each other to stay with the programme. This approach could be achieved through workplace commitments for journeys to work, and through local community groups such as GAP's 'eco-teams' (described above). By building a sense of acting together, strengthening resolve, and providing feedback and praise, eco-teams have been particularly good at helping maintain a changed behaviour until it becomes a habit. Government support for this emerging sector, along with help to spread good practice, is essential.

A complementary approach would be to use the individualised travel-marketing home-visits process, described above, to encourage people to commit to action on a voluntary basis. Once travel advisers have handed over their recommendations, they can ask householders to sign a written (but still voluntary) commitment to carry out some, or all, of them.

City governments and local authorities could even go a step further and follow the example of the city of Aarhus in Denmark, where 90 per cent of participants in a sustainable-transport scheme fulfilled a contract with the municipality to reduce car use. This shows that formal commitments can be very effective at unfreezing entrenched travel habits – especially when combined with the provision of attractive alternatives and incentives (which in Aarhus involved the free use of a bicycle and a bus pass for a year).

Flying

The behaviour changes needed to achieve emission reductions from aviation include taking fewer flights, switching modes of travel and offsetting emissions. These face substantial barriers, ranging from the high status of flying, and people's aspiration and sense of entitlement to travel abroad, to the speed, convenience and low cost of flying versus other modes of transport. Meanwhile, offsetting is hampered by low awareness of the option and, where knowledge of it does exist, a lack of belief that it is meaningful.

Decreasing affordability

The real costs of flying have decreased dramatically over the past 30 years. Further measures need to be taken to arrest this trend and remove a clear financial incentive to fly more and more. Some steps in this direction have already been taken, or will be in a few years. For example, in February 2007, increases in Air Passenger Duty came into effect, and the European Commission announced in late 2006 that from 2011 aviation will be included in the EU Emissions Trading Scheme, both of which will mean an increase in ticket prices.

However, the increases are relatively small, and will deter few from flying. Stronger measures are needed. Air Passenger Duty (APD) should be increased in real terms over time, and resulting revenues matched by expanded investment in low-carbon alternatives. Given the mild level of economic rationalisation in decision-making and the relatively high levels of disposable income, the level of tax would need to be substantial to make a difference.[9]

The Secretary of State for Transport has called for reforms to the Chicago Convention, which regulates international aviation and currently prohibits

---

9   Reforms to APD should also be considered so that it reflects the efficiency of the aircraft and
     the length of the flight (in addition to the headcount of passengers), and hence provides air-
     lines with a greater incentive to fly at full capacity rather than half empty.

the taxation of aviation fuel, with a view to forging agreement on such a tax. Government should continue to press energetically for this reform, at the highest levels.

The Government should also press for effective terms for including aviation in the EU Emissions Trading Scheme, and for the scheme overall to become more effective. These should cover:

- including all flights leaving and entering the European Union
- the auctioning of all allowances through a centrally determined process
- the inclusion of the effects of all greenhouse gases, not just CO_2
- putting in place tough and ever-tighter overall caps on emissions from the sector.

These measures will gradually internalise the environmental costs of flying in the prices charged by airlines, and provide an incentive to fly less. These measures would also benefit one of the main alternatives to flying in relative cost terms: rail travel – particularly high-speed rail travel on some routes – which currently remains comparatively expensive.

Providing convenience

Steps also need to be taken to increase the viability and attractiveness of alternatives to flying. For example, there is a clear case for exploring the possibility of matching increased revenues from Air Passenger Duty with expanded support for investment in rail – especially to increase rail capacity and expand high-speed rail networks, as rail does, and will continue to, require subsidy – much as the London Congestion Charge revenue mostly goes to investment in alternatives to the car.

For UK and European rail to become a more popular mode of holiday travel, the current fragmented European network, with arcane and complex timetables and inconvenient connections, will have to be replaced with a seamless EU-wide rail service, with easy, simple timetabling and ticket prices that rival flights – plus a better service.

Much of this requires better coordination and planning, rather than more capital investment per se. There are already precedents of well-organised high-speed services running between the UK, Belgium, France and Germany, but this is still a massive institutional challenge, with up to 25 separate railway systems running under national jurisdictions in the EU (and, post-privatisation, about 20 different operating companies in the UK alone).

Improving image

However, even if cost disparities reduce, and timetables improve, ground-based travel still suffers from perceptions of inconvenience. One possible approach to this problem might be to reverse the relative status of flying and rail. Flying used to have a high status, but with the advent of mass passenger aviation (especially with deregulation and the rise of budget airlines), the experience of flying is now usually far from glamorous. Today, the increased security arrangements at airports alone have a significantly impact on the passenger experience, requiring extra time and increasing the hassle factor.

In this context, there is an opportunity to bring back the spirit of the Orient Express, and make rail and sea travel enjoyable and aspirational again. This approach will appeal particularly to those who are drawn to new experiences and adventures. For others, celebrity endorsement and use of these modes of travel will be a more powerful driver. For yet others, the attachment to family means that options that offer privacy and safety, such as cabins on boats, will appeal, and could be extended to other modes – for example, private family cabins on trains. Government should work with train operators to develop such options in the future and market them in a targeted way.

Bus and train stations also offer opportunities for redefining travel. The development of airports as part of the flying experience, with huge retail opportunities, has been a major revolution over the past 20 years. Some major railway stations in the UK have taken on this approach to an extent, but in many ways these stations remain Victorian not only in physical structure but in levels of comfort and safety. This needs to change.

There is a role for government in supporting investment in more radical refitting and rebuilding of stations to make them fit for travel in the 21st century, rather than the 19th century. Again, the opportunity for competition with air travel has increased, as new security constraints make airports increasingly prone to long queues and confusion.

Government should also consider providing more funding to market the UK and its coasts, mountains and cities as enticing holiday destinations in their own right that can be reached easily without all the cost and hassle of flying abroad.

Raising understanding
A greater scientific understanding of the contribution of aviation to climate change is emerging. Tonne for tonne, aviation emissions are much more damaging than emissions from energy or road transport. People need to understand the full consequences of their actions when it comes to flying.

Consequently, all advertising for air travel, including holiday packages involving flying, should by law carry bold and visible warnings, like health warnings on tobacco products. Similar warnings should be displayed at all UK airports. As the science develops, it should become possible to attach specific quantitative information about emissions associated with particular flights, both at time of booking and at the departure gate.

The other behaviour change relevant to flying is offsetting. Offsetting suffers from two main problems. One is simply that relatively few people feel sufficiently well informed about it. The other is confusion about whether it really works – a confusion based on real issues, relating to the climate efficacy of tree planting, the security of other offsetting projects and counter-factuals (such as whether your offset payment is going to a project that would not have happened otherwise), and concerns about overheads in offsetting companies – see, for example, Robbins (2006).

The Government needs to take two approaches to offsetting. The first is to provide more information about it, and to set industry standards to give people greater certainty that the way they offset is actually making a difference. It has now produced a voluntary Code of Best Practice for offsetting to UK customers. This should become a mandatory standard.

The other approach that is needed with offsetting is to make use of the psychological fact that people will do what is most convenient. Passengers should thus be required to opt out of offsetting, rather than making offsetting an active choice that only a relatively small minority will make. To illustrate what this would mean, customers buying a plane ticket would be asked to tick a box just before payment saying that they did not want to offset.

However, because of concerns over competitiveness, the only way this will happen is if government requires it of all airlines operating in the UK. This would effectively add to the cost of air travel, but only by a relatively small amount. One option would be to arrange for this offsetting to take the form of the retirement of Certified Emissions Reductions in the European Union Emissions Trading Scheme, thereby tightening up the scheme.

Social proofing
The ultimate objective of government efforts in this sector should be to help create new social norms so that, for example, people feel that it is no longer acceptable to fly within the UK or to neighbouring European countries, to fly long-haul several times a year, and to never offset.

However, creating new social norms takes time. Government could help by setting the example, with new travel guidelines for ministers and officials, and by ensuring that government policies are consistent with the overall objective on flying. This means the Government needs to rethink the 2003 Future of Air Transport White Paper and stop provision for the mass expansion of the UK's national airports, which include a proposed increase in the number of runways. It cannot continue to support the policy of 'predict and supply' demanded by the airline industry.

If other high-profile individuals in society made public pledges not to fly, or to reduce their flying, this would also help create social proof that this is the right way to behave.

The Government should also work with the Carbon Trust to ensure that companies and public organisations put in place travel policies for employees that encourage a responsible approach to flying. In addition, it should increase its support for local and community mutual-support groups (as described above) in which members can set themselves goals or commitments to reduce their flying, monitor and provide feedback on progress, and receive the support they need to meet their objectives. This can play a useful role in helping to foster new social norms.

Step 3: Developing smart and effective communications

The other important element of the framework for climate-friendly behaviour proposed in this report comprises smart communications, which can play a valuable role in supporting interventions to drive behaviour changes across all areas. Communications are no panacea: they will not deliver behaviour change on their own. But they can help inspire people to want to change, make them feel more empowered to do so, and provide them with information on how to go about it.

The UK needs a higher profile, larger-scale, long-running communications campaign on climate change. The Government needs to lead on it, and fund it, possibly with the private sector. However, it should also involve other big players that communicate on this issue – particularly the Energy Saving Trust – and should involve partnerships with relevant companies and campaigning groups.

The campaign needs to have an overarching brand under which different sub-messages appear over time, as with the UK's 'Think!' road safety campaign. The objective would be to help achieve behaviour change, and it should involve asking consumers to change specific behaviours, as well as make them feel that they are able to do so, and telling them how.

The behaviour changes identified as priorities in this chapter should be targeted in such a campaign, but additional communications on them should only be considered if and when the other kinds of policy interventions suggested above are adopted – so that the public has the means and incentives to act on the subject matter of the campaign. The role of communications here is to assist other targeted interventions aimed at bringing about specific behaviour changes, one at a time.

If this campaign is to be successful, it must be created and executed through a systematic and strategic approach. Once the objectives and behaviour changes to be targeted are agreed, government should fund a thorough research and development phase. This should involve members of the public, at its heart, to test and establish for each target behaviour exactly what should be communicated, how, to whom, using which messengers, and through which channels. In fact, throughout the campaign the strategy will need to be tested and adapted using focus groups and deliberative workshops with members of the public.

There is great interest in this type of approach within those government agencies running campaigns – notably the Energy Saving Trust. However, limited funding (reduced in real terms over the last few years) constrains them to the use of more traditional market research surveys. This needs to change.

This is one of several key requirements for effective communications (set out in Chapter 9 of this report) that government has not been good at fulfilling in the past – at least on environmental issues – but which should now be central to any effort in this area. What unites these requirements is an approach that draws on insights from the psychology and sociology of behaviour change described above, rather than from a mainly rationalist approach that focuses on giving more information.

A key challenge for government, and for other agencies communicating on climate change, is to take a more sophisticated approach to knowing and segmenting their audience, so that they can more effectively tailor the campaigns, messages, messengers and communications channels that they use for different subgroups of the population. Previous campaigns on climate change have tended to think in general terms about 'the public', or about particular segments by socio-economic or consumer group, using systems such as MOSAIC.

These types of segmentation are useful, but need to be complemented by psychographic models based on the differing psychological characteristics of the population, allowing communications to tap accurately and effectively into the motivations of particular groups (see Box 10.3).

Another technique that the Government and others communicating on climate change should use in designing communications campaigns is strategic frame analysis. This encourages the framing of approaches using language relating to the higher-level values subscribed to by target audiences. (To see how this has been applied for use in the United States, see Box 10.4 below.) Other obvious guidelines for effective communications include:

- Keep approaches clear and simple.
- Don't preach.
- Use personal and emotional appeal and the power of the image.
- Make behaviour changes appear aspirational.
- Give people an inspiring aim.
- Make people feel good, useful and important.

In the words of Ereaut and Signit (2006: 27):

'It is not enough simply to produce yet more messages to convince people of the reality of climate change and urge them to act. We need to work in different and more sophisticated ways, harnessing tools

Box 10.3: Using psychology to design communications

The 'values modes' segmentation model described in Chapter 9 of this report identifies three broad groups of people based on Maslow's theory of psychological needs, which can be further sub-divided into 12 different groups. Each of these groups has differing motivations and thus requires very different communications approaches.

Pioneers (35 per cent of the UK population) have 'inner directed' needs: they seek an ethical basis for life, and they are society's natural activists. Aesthetics are important to them, but status is not. They are casual about finances, seeing the purpose of money as being to buy quality, and seek new experiences.

If climate change were presented to them as a long-term global problem and they were offered a technological solution to it, they would be more likely to adopt it because it would be the right thing to do, knowing that they were doing it for a good cause (Rose *et al* 2005). For them, communications on climate-friendly behaviour would emphasise the ethics of such behaviour. However, it could also make an appeal to other values – by, for example, emphasising that by investing in micro-renewables they would be buying a quality alternative product, or that by going on holiday by train they would be at the cutting edge of a new kind of travel adventure.

Prospectors (44 per cent of the UK population) have esteem or 'outer-directed' needs: they live for today and seek psychological rewards in status and achievement. They are not worried about security, as they are already financially secure. People within this category underpin consumer society.

This group would be more likely to think of climate change as a problem if it was presented as a threat to their prospects for achievement and success. Tailoring an approach to the values of this group to motivate climate-friendly behaviour would involve an appeal to act or adopt a technological solution because it was in fashion, was used by celebrities, would help them look successful, would add value to their home, was made by a blue-chip company or could be changed in line with the latest trend (ibid).

The emphasis would be on new ways of spending and acting. Ereaut and Segnit (2006: 28) argue that this group offers 'a ripe opportunity for climate-related behaviour change'. They continue: 'People like this want to feel special, and are accustomed to achieving this feeling through what they do and what they buy, rather than what they do not do or do not buy.'

For example, in motivating this group to invest in a hybrid car or micro-renewables, the implicit message would be 'Buy this and you'll be the envy of your peers.' People in this group might also be open to a service that offered a 'green makeover' of their homes on status grounds. They will also be more open to certain behaviour changes than others – for example, buying offsets, rather than no longer flying abroad.

Settlers (21 per cent of the UK population) have sustenance-driven needs, and do not like anything that threatens identity, belonging, security or safety. They are motivated by the need to protect what they have, and tend to have a strong comfort focus on their homes. Financial security is a high priority, and they spend their money more cautiously.

Settlers are likely to be the last to change. For this group, communications would need to emphasise that climate change was a problem because it would affect their family, local area, identity and traditions. They would need to be persuaded that the country's leaders were acting on the issue, and that everyone else was doing so, in order for the required behaviour to appear 'normal' and being done by 'people like them' (Rose *et al* 2005).

Examples of values-based appeals for climate-friendly behaviour might be that fitting insulation can save them money, keep them warm and improve the value of their home, or that switching to bio-fuels will save them having to pay fuel duty. Wherever a large purchase is needed (for example, on condensing boilers), a carefully thought-through package of financing would be needed.

and concepts used by brand advertisers, to make it not dutiful or obedient to be climate friendly, but desirable.'

Another key challenge for communications is to help make people feel that acting is worthwhile because it will make a difference. Existing climate communications in the UK do not do this well. Chapter 4 of this report shows how the widely used alarmism repertoire on climate change creates fear without providing a sense of agency, thus demotivating people. The other dominant approach focuses on the small actions that people can take and is not compelling enough to motivate action either – especially when juxtaposed with alarmist messages emphasising the huge scale of the problem. The contrast between the scale of the problem and the solutions presented is so wide that people are not convinced that they can make a difference.

This analysis should influence communications policy in several different ways. First, the primary focus of communications should now be on the solutions rather than the problem. Communications need to treat the argument on the nature of the problem as having been won: that climate change exists, and is real, and the facts so taken for granted they need not be spoken (Ereaut and Segnit 2006).

Box 10.4: Framing climate-change communications in the United States

The FrameWorks Institute (2001) developed the following proposals for US climate communicators using the strategic frame approach:

- First, place the issue in the context of higher-level values, including responsibility, stewardship, competence, vision and ingenuity. Hence, for example, 'American innovation can address this problem if we do the responsible thing and start planning now rather than procrastinate.'

- Use messengers associated with suggested frames, such as:

  - business planners and parents to evoke responsible management
  - business and science and technology innovators to advance solutions
  - religious leaders to promote stewardship
  - scientists to explain the causes of global warming

- Introduce a simplifying model, analogy or metaphor to help the public understand how global warming works – a 'conceptual hook' so that they can make sense of information about the issue. An example is the concept of the 'ozone hole'. For global warming, instead of the 'greenhouse gas effect', talk about the CO_2 blanket and CO_2 heat-trap as a simple mechanism that can set up appropriate reasoning.

- Include consequences without appearing extreme in size or scale. Put humans at the centre, make the messages fit with personal experience, convey regional examples, and reduce the timelines – talk about what will happen in 20 years' time, rather than 200 years.

- Evoke solutions, creating a way for people to understand that solutions are possible and effective, and make an explicit call to action. Appeal to people as problem solvers, and take care to appropriately match the solution to the problem.

Source: Adapted from FrameWorks Institute 2001

Instead, the focus should be on the large-scale solutions that people can take and the impact these can have. Techniques must be used to inject the discourse with the energy it currently lacks (see Box 10.5). More widely, communications strategies should be devised to address or eliminate each of the possible excuses or 'outs' that people may make or seek, in order to avoid having to take the action being asked of them.

Government also needs to fund research into precisely who the target audiences respect, listen to or learn from most (broken down by the combined socio-economic and psychographic segmentation), to ensure that the right messengers can be used. Generally, communications that emanate from authority sources and that continue to instruct, or even cajole, are likely to be less successful than those that work with the emerging dynamic,

Box 10.5: Ordinary heroism: harnessing myth to inspire action

The problem of disparity of scale – between the enormity of the problem, as depicted in the alarmism repertoire, and the small individual actions that can be taken to address it – is potentially an opportunity. This disparity is currently the source of wry juxtapositions: 'Unplug your TV, save the planet'. With the right approach, one could properly harness this disparity by using myth to inject the discourse with energy and reconcile seemingly irreconcilable cultural truths.

Opposing the enormous forces of climate change requires something superhuman or heroic. Science is not enough – especially when scientists argue among themselves. What is needed is something more magical, more mythical. Many strong and successful brands have a kind of 'myth' at their core – they appear to reconcile things that are normally impossible to reconcile. Our suggestion is that the key powerful myth for action on climate change is 'ordinary heroism'.

In this model of communication, the cultural norms (in other words, what we normally expect to be true) are that heroes – the ones who act, are powerful and carry out great deeds – are extraordinary, while ordinary mortals either do nothing or do bad things. The mythical position – the one that occupies the seemingly impossible space – is that of 'ordinary hero'.

What is potentially powerful about the 'ordinary heroism' myth is that it feels rooted in British culture – from the Dunkirk spirit to Live Aid. Conscious and concerted formulation of ordinary heroism might offer even more powerful solutions. It is easy to imagine it providing fertile ground for creative communications.

Source: Adapted from Ereaut and Segnit 2006

NB: Since this report was published, the Energy Saving Trust has implemented some of its findings, most notably the 'ordinary hero' approach, in its more recent campaign, which began in October 2006.

---

which favours bottom-up or horizontal authority. Increasingly, people trust each other (even those they have not met) more than governments and other institutions (Ereaut and Segnit 2006).

Similarly, research is needed into precisely what the different target audiences read, watch or listen to most (again, segmented by socio-economic and psychographic group), so that climate communications efforts can be targeted through the most appropriate channels. Corporations do this well; government less so (with some exceptions, such as the 'Think!' campaign).

At the same time, government should ensure that any campaign has a national presence – most easily achieved through television – to convey the sense that the issue is of national importance, and that the whole nation is part of solving it. At the other extreme, government should make sure funding is provided for as much face-to-face, person-to-person engagement as possible (in the ways described above), as this is more motivating.

Even well-designed and targeted campaigns to persuade people to adopt climate-friendly behaviour will take time to work, and will require repetition. This means that government needs to make a large-scale, long-term financial commitment to a communications campaign on climate change, promising at least £8 million per year for five years as a first step. Additional initial funding will also be needed to deliver and test the proposed combined socio-economic and psychographic segmentation approach.

A final key element of the approach to communications is the need for consistency. A campaign clearly needs to achieve internal consistency with regards to the messages it produces. But it also requires efforts to work with the mainstream media, given the extent of media influence, to encourage supportive approaches – as well as a commitment to introduce new standards on commercial advertising of climate-unfriendly products (see above).

Lastly, it is critical that government's own behaviour is consistent with what it is asking the public to do. People mistrust and ignore exhortations to behave environmentally if these appear at odds with the behaviour of government, or are inconsistent with policy measures coming from government. A recent assessment of the Government's record on energy and travel in its own operations is patchy (SDC 2005c). This needs to change.

Credible leadership requires that government takes every opportunity to exemplify behaviour change. At the very least, the Government should make sure it meets the targets launched in June 2006 by the Prime Minister for sustainable operations on the government estate, and in the Sustainable Procurement Action Plan (DEFRA 2006c). But it should also go further, by taking the actions suggested above to boost the extent of on-site microgeneration and by setting up travel plans that cut down on car use and flying. It also needs to reassess its policies on road building and airport expansion, so that efforts to encourage people to drive and fly less are not undermined. The policies and practices of all departments must be in line with climate change objectives.

A new partnership

As well as the actions outlined above, government leadership is also relevant in an institutional sense. The agenda set out in this report may be delivered largely through local government, community groups, eco-auditors working for civil society organisations, social enterprises and, indeed, large corporations. Government will have to think about new ways of engaging with and supporting these actors.

National government can clearly help by promoting initiatives led by these players, and by providing them with dependable funding streams. But more needs to be known about:

- how else community-based social marketing strategies, in particular, should be supported
- how government should relate to such initiatives
- what level of resources they require for success.

The Government might even consider setting up community groups itself, to deliver services on the ground – as the Canadian government did in the 1990s.

New models of engaging with the private sector – for example, through groups such as the Climate Group and the Corporate Leaders Group on Climate Change – offer new opportunities for the Government to achieve its objectives, too. But it must also think carefully about how to set frameworks with the right kinds of incentives, that produce aspirational low-carbon services and products.

Government itself must also remain visible. People look to government to take a lead, so in all these different forms of delivery and engagement it must be clear that government is playing the lead role.

Institutional change will probably be needed, too. A systematic and strategic approach to behavioural change across all areas of policy calls for a new, centralised unit to be set up in Whitehall that understands behaviour change and how to deliver non-traditional forms of policy, and is capable of driving this change agenda through. This unit would be tasked with auditing all government policy to establish shortcomings, recommend improvements, and ensure a strategic and coordinated approach exists to stimulating climate-friendly behaviour across government. It should also engage with the public.

One of the first tasks of this unit should be to commission a large-scale deliberative event with 1000 members of the public from across the UK, recruited along psychometric as well as socio-economic lines (as described above). By engaging people in problem solving and treating them as partners in the co-creation of policy in this area, people will feel more empowered to make a difference, their trust in outcomes will be increased, and the quality of policymaking will be improved as a better understanding is reached of what would best motivate different groups of people to act.

This unit should sit outside any one particular department. It could be housed in the newly formed Government Office of Climate Change, whose focus on analysis and policy could help it devise the right strategy. It should also work closely with the Government's current main delivery agency for behaviour change – the Energy Saving Trust. The EST itself should be given expanded and dependable funding into the future so that it can increase its capacity to support the public in adopting climate-friendly behaviour. Any such additional funding should be conditional on an assessment of the EST's effectiveness, and its adoption of the direction of travel outlined in this report.

Conclusions

The central message of this report is that climate-friendly behaviour change (as with all behaviour change) is driven not only by policies appealing to the rational side of human nature – especially information and pricing – but also by a range of social and psychological factors. Already, much is known about these factors, and major corporations and others have used them successfully to sell products and services for years. It is time for climate policy to do so too, by adopting the new framework for climate-friendly behaviour outlined in this report.

This framework opens up a larger range of options for engaging with the public. Some of these options will prove fruitful, while others may not. But government urgently needs to begin considering them seriously. If we fail to change behaviours in a significant way in the next few years, by using this new palette of options, then we may have to fall back on yet more radical (and possibly more costly) policy options, such as introducing a form of carbon rationing for individuals.

Before change is imposed on that scale, people deserve the right to be given the possibility to change. A growing proportion of the public is clearly concerned about the climate problem, and good policy should ensure that they are empowered to do something about the situation for themselves. Exhortations to behave differently will not work. Approaches to enable people to adopt alternative forms of behaviour, by making them cheaper, more visible and more attractive, are now urgently needed. Then the positive energy that people can bring to bear by acting together may truly be harnessed to beat this problem.

References

Note: web references correct March 2007

ACE (Association for the Conservation of Energy) (2006) 'Inquiry into the pre-budget report 2005', memorandum London: ACE

Ajzen I and Fishbein M (1980) *Understanding Attitudes and Predicting Social Behaviour*, Englewood Cliffs, NJ: Prentice Hall

Alexander Ballard and Associates/Rosslyn Research Ltd (2005) *How Can Local Authorities Stimulate and Support Behavioural Change in Response to Climate Change?* Winchester: Hampshire County Council

Anable J (2005) '"Complacent car addicts" or "aspiring environmentalists"? Identifying travel behaviour segments using attitude theory', *Transport Policy* vol 12: 65–78

Anable J, Cairns S, Sloman L, Newson C, Kirkbride A and Goodwin P (2005) *Smarter Choices and Carbon Emissions*, scoping study, London: DfT

Anable J, Lane B and Kelay T (2006) *An Evidence Base Review of Public Attitudes to Climate Change and Transport Behaviour*, London: Department for Transport

Andersen J (1982) 'Acquisition of Cognitive Skill', *Psychological Review*, vol 89: 369–406

Anderson S and Stradling S (2004) *Attitudes Towards Car Use and Modal Shift in Scotland*, Edinburgh: Transport Research Planning Group, Scottish Executive

Atkins C (2005) 'Written answer in the House of Commons', 24 February, data from the Retail Price Index, Office for National Statistics, available at: www.publications.parliament.uk/pa/cm200405/cmhansrd/cm050224/text/50224w06.htm

Automobile Association (AA) Trust (2006) 'Fuel price reports 2004–2006,' online resource, AA Trust, available at www.theaa.com/motoring_advice/fuel

Baer P and Mastrandrea M (2006) *High Stakes: Designing emissions pathways to reduce the risk of dangerous climate change*, London: ippr

Ballard D (2005) 'Using learning processes to promote change for sustainable development', *Action Research*, vol 3 (2): 135–156

Bamberg S (1999) 'Explaining and changing car driver's behaviour: a psychological approach', keynote speech, 16 September

Bandura A (1977) 'Self-efficacy: Toward a unifying theory of behavioral change' Psychological Review, March, vol 84 (2): 191–215

Barker A (2003) *Attitudes to renewable energy: final report*, London: COI

Barker K (2004) *Barker Review of Housing Supply: Securing our future housing needs*, final report, London: HM Treasury/ODPM

Barker K (2006) *Barker Review of Land Use Planning: Final Report*, London: Barker Review of Planning

Bartillat L and Retallack S (2003) *STOP*, Paris: Le Seuil

BBC (2003) 'Commuters lured by luxury bus', news update, London: BBC, available at: http://news.bbc.co.uk/1/hi/england/north_yorkshire/3218685.stm

BBC (2004) Climate change poll, carried out by ICM for BBC News Online

Bem D (1972) 'Social perception theory' in L Berkowitz (ed) *Advances in Experimental Social Psychology* 6, London: Academic Press

Bibbings J (2004a) *Climate Concern: Attitudes to climate change and windfarms in Wales*, Cardiff: Welsh Consumer Council/Friends of theEarth Cymru

Bibbings J (2004b) *A High Price to Pay?*, Cardiff: Welsh Consumer Council

Bickerstaff K and Walker G (2001) 'Public understandings of air pollution: the "localisation" of environmental risk', *Global Environmental Change* vol 11: 133–145

Bickerstaff K, Lorenzoni I, Pidgeon N, Poortinga W and Simmons P (2006) *Re-framing Nuclear Power in the UK Energy Debate: Nuclear power, climate change mitigation and radioactive waste*, Norwich: Centre for Environmental Risk, University of East Anglia

Bird J and Morris J (2006) *Steering Through Change: Winning the debate on road pricing*, London: ippr

Bird J and Vigor A (2006) *Charging Forward? A review of public attitudes towards road pricing in the UK*, London: ippr

Blair T (2006) Letter to Stop Climate Chaos, available at www.stopclimatechaos.org/documents/tb_letter_to_scc_280206.pdf

Boardman B, Darby S, Killip G, Hinnells M, Jardine C, Palmer J and Sinden G (2005) *The 40% House*, Oxford: Environmental Change Institute

Bonsall P (2002) *Car Share and Car Clubs: Potential impacts*, final report, DLTR/Motorists' Forum, Leeds: Institute of Transport Studies, University of Leeds

Bonsall P, Stone V, Stewart J and Dix M (2006) *Consumer Behaviour and Pricing Structures: Final report on qualitative research*, London: Department for Transport

BRE (2004) *Assessment of Energy Efficiency Impact of Building Regulations Compliance*, London: EST

British Photovoltaic Association (2006) *A Guide to Photovoltaic Systems*, available at: www.greenenergy.org.uk/pvuk2/technology/index.html

British Wind Energy Association (BWEA) (2006) 'BWEA statistics', web resource, London: BWEA, available at: www.bwea.com/ukwed

Brook Lyndhurst (2004) *Bad Habits and Hard Choices: In search of sustainable lifestyles*, London: Brook Lyndhurst

Brook Lyndhurst/MORI (2001) *Household Waste Behaviour in London*, Skipton: Resource Recovery Forum

Brook Lyndhurst/MORI/Upstream for London Renewables (2003) *Attitudes to Renewable Energy in London*, London: Greater London Authority

Brown G (2007) Speech by the Chancellor of the Exchequer, the Rt Hon Gordon Brown MP, to the Green Alliance, 13 March, HMT, London

Burgess J, Harrison C and Filius P (1998) 'Environmental communication and the cultural politics of environmental citizenship', *Environment and Planning A*, vol 30: 1445–1460

Cairns S, Sloman L, Newson C, Anable J, Kirkbride A and Goodwin P (2004) *Smarter Choices – Changing the way we travel*, London: DfT

Cairns S and Newson C (2006) *Predict and Decide: Aviation, climate change and UK policy*, Oxford: Environmental Change Institute

Calder F (2005) *Communicating Climate Change: A paper for the International Climate Change Taskforce*, London: ippr

CFIT (2004b) *The Bus Industry – Encouraging local delivery*, London: CFIT

Civil Aviation Authority (CAA) (2004) *UK Airport Statistics 2004*, London: CAA, available at: www.caa.co.uk/docs/80/airport_data/2005Annual/Table_02_2_Summary_of_Activity_at_UK_Airports.pdf

Chawla L (1998) 'Significant life experiences revisited: a review of research on sources of pro-environmental sensitivity', *The Journal of Environmental Education*, vol 29: 11

Chawla L (1999) 'Life paths into effective environmental action', *The Journal of Environmental Education*, 31: 15

Civil Aviation Authority (CAA) (2005) *Demand for Outbound Leisure Air Travel and its Key Drivers*, London: CAA

Climate Challenge Communication Initiative (2007) 'Climate Challenge Fund projects', web page, London: DEFRA, available at: www.climatechallenge.gov.uk/whats_being_done/projects.aspx

Cohen S (2001) *States of Denial: Knowing about atrocities and suffering*, Cambridge: Polity Press

Collins J, Thomas G, Willis R and Wilsdon J (2003) *Carrots, Sticks and Sermons: Influencing public behaviour for environmental goals*, London: Demos/Green Alliance

Commission for Integrated Transport (CFIT) (2004a) *High Speed Rail: International comparisons*, London: CFIT

Cooke V (2003) *Who Cares What the Person on the Clapham Omnibus Thinks?*, London: Opinion Leader Research

Cottam H and Leadbetter C (2004) *Health: Co-creating services*, RED paper 01, London: Design Council

Dade P and Rose C (2005) *Values And Voter Survey 2005, Part 1: Mapping psychological change in the UK*, London: Cultural Dynamics and Marketing Ltd/Campaign Strategy Ltd

Darby S (2005) *Making it Obvious: Designing feedback into energy consumption*, Oxford: Environmental Change Institute, University of Oxford

Darby S (2006) *The Effectiveness of Feedback on Energy Consumption*, review for DEFRA of the literature on metering, billing and direct displays, Oxford: Environmental Change Institute

Darnton A (2004a) *Energy Saving Trust Audiences*, final report of desk research, London: EST

Darnton A (2004b) *The Impact of Sustainable Development on Public Behaviour*, report 1 of desk research, London: DEFRA

Darnton A (2004c) *Driving Public Behaviours for Sustainable Lifestyles*, report 2 of desk research, London: DEFRA

Darnton A (2005) *Appendix 1: Public Understanding of Climate Change*, London: FUTERRA Sustainability Communications Ltd

Department of Communities and Local Government (DCLG) (2006a) *Review of Planning Policy*

Statement 22: Renewable energy policies in emerging development plans, London: DCLG, available at: www.communities.gov.uk/index.asp?id=1500549

DCLG (2006b) *Housing Statistics 2006*, London: TSO, available at: www.communities.gov.uk/pub/234/HousingStatistics2006_id1505234.pdf

Department for Environment, Food and Rural Affairs (DEFRA) (1998) *Energy Efficiency in the Domestic Sector*, technical support paper, London: DEFRA, available at: www.defra.gov.uk/environment/consult/climatechange/technical/4.htm

DEFRA (2002) *Survey of Public Attitudes to Quality of Life and to the Environment – 2001*, London: Office of National Statistics/DEFRA

DEFRA (2004a) *Energy Efficiency: The Government's plan for action*, London: DEFRA

DEFRA (2004b) *Energy Efficiency Commitment 2005–2008: Illustrative mix of possible measures*, London: DEFRA, available at: www.defra.gov.uk/environment/energy/eec/pdf/measuremix.pdf

DEFRA (2005) 'DEFRA urges "green holidaymaking"', press release, 25 July, London: DEFRA, available at: www.defra.gov.uk/news/latest/2005/environ-0725.htm

DEFRA (2006a) *Attitudes to Climate Change: Wave 3*, London: DEFRA, available at: www.climate-challenge.gov.uk/multimedia/climate_change_toplines_wave3.pdf

DEFRA (2006b) *The Energy Efficiency Commitment April 2008 to March 2011: Initial consultation*, London: DEFRA

DEFRA (2006c) *Climate Change: The UK programme 2006*, London: DEFRA

DEFRA (2006d) 'British Gas extends council tax rebate programme to nearly 1 million homes', news release, 13 March, London: DEFRA/British Gas, available at: www.defra.gov.uk/news/2006/060313a.htm

DEFRA (2006e) 'Sustainable operations on the government estate', web update, London: DEFRA, available at: www.sustainable-development.gov.uk/government/estates/index.htm#targets

DEFRA (2006f) *Global Atmosphere Statistics. Estimated emissions of carbon dioxide by IPCC source category, type of fuel and end user: 1970–2004*, London: DEFRA, available at: www.defra.gov.uk/environment/statistics/globatmos/download/xls/gatb05.xls

DEFRA (2006g) *The Energy Efficiency Commitment April 2008 to March 2011: Initial consultation*,London: DEFRA

DEFRA (2006h) *An Environmental Behaviours Strategy for DEFRA*, scoping report, London: DEFRA

DEFRA (2007a) *Consultation on Establishing a Voluntary Code of Best Practice for the Provision of Carbon Offsetting to UK Customers*, London: DEFRA

DEFRA (2007b) *Statistical Release: 2005 UK climate change sustainable development indicator and greenhouse gas emissions final figures*, London: DEFRA

DEFRA/DfT (2005) 'UK backs European commission to include aviation emissions in the EU emissions trading scheme', news release, 27 September, London: DEFRA/DfT

Department for Transport (DfT) (2002a) *Powering Future Vehicles Strategy*, London: DfT

DfT (2002b) *Attitudes to Walking and Cycling*, results from the Office for National Statistics (ONS) October 2002 Omnibus Survey, London: DfT

DfT (2003a) *Comparative Colour-Coded Labels for Passenger Cars*, London: MORI/DfT

DfT (2003b) *The Future of Air Transport*, HM Government White Paper, Norwich: The Stationery Office

DfT (2003c) *Assessing the Impact of Graduated Vehicle Excise Duty*, qualitative report, London: MORI/DfT deleted c, no d

DfT (2004a) *Powering Future Vehicles: The government strategy*, second annual report, London: DfT

DfT (2004b) *The Future of Transport: A network for 2030*, HM Government White Paper, Norwich: The Stationery Office

DfT (2004c) *Feasibility Study of Road Pricing in the UK*, report to the Secretary of State for Transport, London: DfT

DfT (2005a) *Transport Statistics Great Britain 2005 edition*, 31st edition, London: The Stationery Office

DfT (2005b) *Transport Statistics Bulletin. Regional transport statistics: 2005*, London: DfT

DfT (2005c) *UK Report to the Commission on Biofuels 2005*, London: DfT

DfT (2005d) *Future of Transport Traffic Summary. Traffic growth on year 2000 by vehicle type*, London: DfT, available at:www.dft.gov.uk/stellent/groups/dft_foi/documents/page/dft_foi_036820.pdf

DfT (2005e) *Delivery of the National Cycling Strategy: A review*, London: DfT

DfT (2005f) *Transport Statistics Bulletin: National travel survey 2004*, Norwich: The Stationery Office

DfT (2006a) *Public Experiences of and Attitudes Towards Air Travel*, London: DfT

DfT (2006b) 'Freedom of information request for number of passengers travelling from UK airports to foreign destinations', online briefing, 24 April 2006, London: DfT, available at: www.dft.gov.uk/stellent/groups/dft_foi/documents/divisionhomepage/611569.hcsp

DfT (2006c) *Attitudes to Climate Change and the Impact of Transport. Results from the Office for National Statistics October 2005 Omnibus Survey*, London: DfT

DfT (2006d) *Air Transport White Paper Progress Report 2006*, London: DfT

Department for Trade and Industry (DTI) (2005a) *Fuel Poverty Advisory Group (for England) Fourth Annual Report 2005*, London: DTI

DTI (2005b) *Microgeneration Strategy and Low Carbon Buildings Programme: Consultation*, London: DTI

DTI (2005c) *Analysis of Responses to the Microgeneration Strategy and Low Carbon Buildings Programme Consultation*, London: Future Energy Solutions/DTI

DTI (2005d) *Electricity and Gas: The Electricity (Fuel Mix Disclosure) Regulations 2005*, statutory instrument 2005 no 391, Norwich: The Stationery Office

DTI (2006a) *Our Energy Challenge: Securing clean affordable energy for the long-term*, Energy Review consultation document, London: DTI

DTI (2006b) *Our Energy Challenge: Power from the people*, microgeneration strategy, London: DTI

DTI (2006c) 'Energy consumption tables' web resource, London: DTI, available at: www.dti.gov.uk/energy/statistics/publications/energy-consumption/domestic-tables/page18071.html

DTI (2006d) *UK Energy and CO_2 Emissions Projections*, updated projections to 2020: part 1, July 2006, London: DTI

DTI (2006e) *Digest of UK Energy Statistics 2006*, London: DTI

DTI (2006f) 'Wicks gives a helping hand to green householders', press release, 27 October 2006, London: DTI. Available at: www.gnn.gov.uk/environment/fullDetail.asp?ReleaseID=237854&NewsAreaID=2&NavigatedFromDepartment=False

DTI (2007a) 'DTI – energy statistics', press release, 4 January 2007, London: DTI

DTI (2007b) 'DTI – energy statistics', press release, 29 March 2007, London: DTI

Diekmann A and Franzen A (1996) 'Einsicht in okologische zusammenhange und umweltverhalten' in Kaufmann-Hayoz R and Di Giulio A (eds) *Umweltproblem Mensch: Humanwissenschaftliche zusammenhänge zu umweltverantwortlichem handeln*, Bern: Verlag Paul Haupt

Diekmann A and Preisendörfer P (1992) 'Persönliches umweltverhalten: die diskrepanz zwischen anspruch und wirklichkeit', *Kölner Zeitschrift für Soziologie und Sozialpsychologie*, vol 44: 226–251

Downing Street (2007) 'PM's climate change interview with Sky', web update, London: Downing Street, available at: www.pm.gov.uk/output/Page10715.asp

Dudleston A, Stradling S and Anable J (2005) *Public Perceptions of Travel Awareness – Phase 3*, research findings no 202/2005, Edinburgh: Scottish Executive Social Research

Duffy B, Hall S, Williams M (2005) *Who do You Believe: Trust in government information*, London: MORI

EDF Energy (2005) *Energy Issues*, London: MORI/EDF

EHCS (2007) *English House Condition Survey 2005, Headline Report*, London: DCLG

Ekins P (2003) *An Introduction to the ESRC New Opportunities Programme Environment and Human Behaviour*, London: Policy Studies Institute, available at: www.psi.org.uk/ehb/introduction.html

Ekins P and Dresner S (2004) *Green Taxes and Charges: Reducing their impact on low-income households*, York: Joseph Rowntree Foundation

Energy Saving Trust (EST) (2004a) *Energy Efficiency Brand and Advertising Tracker Pre-wave*, London: COI/EST

EST (2004b) *Consultation on Transport Energy Clean Vehicle Grant Programmes: Energy Saving Trust response*, London: EST

EST (2004c) *CAfE Evaluation Report*, London: TNS Social/EST

EST (2005a) 'Energy Saving Trust pre-campaign questionnaire for 2005/6 marketing strategy', London: EST

EST (2005b) *Potential for Microgeneration Study and Analysis*, London: EST/Econnect/ElementEnergy/DTI

EST (2005c) *Fiscal Measures and Energy Efficient Lighting*, update, October 2005, London: EST

EST (2005d) *Consumer Attitudes Towards Microgeneration Technologies*, report by Haslam Associates, London: EST

EST (2005e) *Energy Efficiency Partnership for Homes Annual Review 2004/2005*, London: EST

EST (2005f) *Potential for Micro-generation: Study and analysis*, London: EST

EST (2006a) *Energy Saving Trust's response to 'Our Energy Challenge – Securing clean affordable energy for the long term'*, London: EST

EST (2006b) 'Types of renewable energy technology', web page, London: EST, available at: www.est.org.uk/myhome/generating/types/

EST (2006c) *Practical Help News*, Summer 2006, issue 20, EST: London

EST (2006d) *The Rise of The Machines: A review of energy using products in the home from the 1970s to today*, London: EST

EST (2006e) *Habits of a Lifetime: European energy usage report*, London: EST

EST (2007) 'Five simple ways to unlock hidden value', web page, London: EST, available at: www.est.org.uk/myhome/hiddenvalue/unlock/

EST/IEEP (2004) *Passenger Cars: CO_2 emissions and vehicle excise duty*, London: EST/IEEP

Environment Agency (2006) *Marketing Strategies to Promote Retrofitting Behaviour*, London: Environment Agency (unpublished)

Environmental Transport Association (ETA) (2006) 'Britons lacking hybrid awareness', news release, 31 March, Weybridge: ETA, available at: www.eta.co.uk/news/newsview.asp?n=493

Ereaut G and Segnit N (2006) *Warm Words: How are we telling the climate story and can we tell it better?* London: ippr

ESPACE (2005) *How Can Local Authorities Stimulate and Support Behavioural Change in Response to Climate Change?* Winchester: Hampshire County Council

Eurobarometer (2005) *The Attitudes of European Citizens Towards Tnvironment*, special Eurobarometer 217 Brussels: European Commission

European Commission (2003) *Proposal for a Directive of the European Parliament and of the Council on Energy End-use Efficiency and Energy Services*, Brussels: European Commission

European Commission (2005a) 'Climate change: Commission proposes strategy to curb greenhouse gas emissions from air travel', press release, 27 September 2005, Brussels: European Commission

European Commission (2005b) *Environmentally-friendly Design of Energy-using Products: Framework directive for setting eco-design requirements for energy-using products*, Brussels: European Commission

European Conference of Ministers of Transport (ECMT)/Organisation for Economic Cooperation and Development (OECD) (1995) *Urban Travel and Sustainable Development*, Paris: OECD

European Environment Agency (2001) *Renewable Energy – Success stories*, environmental issues report no 27, Copenhagen: EEA

European Federation for Transport and Environment/Climate Action Network Europe (2006) *Clearing the Air – The myth and reality of aviation and climate change*, Brussels: EFTE/CANE

Every L, Grayling T, Preston J and Anderson R (2004) *Options for Delivering the Merseyside Bus Strategy*, report prepared for Merseytravel, London: ippr

Fenton Communications (2001) *Now Hear This: Nine laws of successful advocacy communications*, Washington DC: Fenton Communications

FrameWorks Institute (2001) *Talking Global Warming: A FrameWorks message memo*, Washington DC: FrameWorks Institute

Friends of the Earth (FoE) (2004a) *Friends of the Earth Guide to Green Electricity Tariffs 2004*, London: FoE

FoE (2004b) *Oil Prices, Fuel Tax and Climate Change*, briefing, London: FoE

FoE (2005) *Green Electricity Tariffs*, briefing, London: FoE

Fuel Poverty Advisory Group (for England) (2005) *Fourth Annual Report*, London: DTI

Futerra (2005a) *The Rules of the Game: Evidence base for the climate change communications strategy*, London: Futerra

Futerra (2005b) *UK Communications Strategy on Climate Change*, paper prepared for the Climate Change Communications Working Group, London: Futerra

Futerra (2006) *New Rules, New Game: Communications tactics for climate change*, London: Futerra

Future Laboratory (2005) *20/20 Futures Energy and Waste in an Age of Excess*, London: Energy Saving Trust/Future Laboratory, unpublished

Garnett T (2003) *Wise Moves: Exploring the relationship between food, transport and CO2*, London: Transport 2000

Gladwell M (2000) *The Tipping Point: How little things can make a big difference*, Boston: Little Brown and Company

Glaister S and Graham D (2000) *The Effect of Fuel Prices on Motorists*, report commissioned by the AA Motoring Policy Unit and the UK Petroleum Industry Association, Hampshire: AA Motoring Trust

Global Action Plan (GAP) (2006) *Global Action Plan – Changing Environmental Behaviour: A review of evidence from GAP*, London: Global Action Plan, available at: www.globalactionplan.org.uk/documents/GAP%20Behaviour%20Change%20Report.pdf

Globescan International (2006) '30-country poll finds worldwide consensus that climate change is a serious problem', online news story, London: Globescan, available at:

www.globescan.com/news_archives/csr_climatechange.html

Gordon W (2002) *Brand Green: Mainstream or forever niche?* London: Green Alliance

Government of Canada (2006) 'One tonne challenge: take action on climate change', presentation to the C4/OTC conference, Ottawa

Graham A (2006) 'Have the major forces driving leisure airline traffic changed?', *Journal of Air Transport Management* vol 12: 14–20

Graham V (2007) *Reality or Rhetoric? Green tariffs for domestic consumers* London: National Consumer Council

Grayling T, Sansom N and Foley J (2004) *In the Fast Lane: Fair and effective road user charging in Britain*, London: ippr

Grayling T, Lawrence T and Gibbs T (2005) *Climate Commitment: Meeting the UK's 2010 CO_2 emissions target*, London: ippr

Grayling T, Gibbs T and Castle B (2006) *Tailpipe Trading: How to include road transport in the EU Emissions Trading Scheme*, London: ippr

Green E and Stone V (2004) *Public Attitudes to Road Pricing in the UK: A qualitative study*, London: DfT/BMRB Social Research, available at: www.dft.gov.uk/stellent/groups/dft_roads/documents/page/dft_roads_029786.doc

Greenwald A (1968) 'Cognitive learning, cognitive responses to persuasion and attitude change' in Greenwald A, Brock T and Ostrom T (eds) *Psychological Foundations of Attitudes*, New York: Academic Press

Halpern D (2005) 'Something for something: personal responsibility meets behavioural economics', *Public Policy Research*, vol 12 (1): 22-29

Halpern D, Bates C, Mulgan G, Aldridge S, Beales S and Heathfield A (2004) *Personal Responsibility and Changing Behaviour: The state of knowledge and its implications for public policy*, London: Cabinet Office

Her Majesty's Treasury (HMT) (2005) *Total Expenditure on Services by function: 1987/88 to 2004/05*, London: HMT, available at: www.hm-treasury.gov.uk/media/00E/0C/Latest_functional_data_PBR_2005.xls

HMT (2006a) *Budget 2006: Economic and fiscal strategy report and financial statement and budget report*, London: HMT

HMT (2006b) *2006 Pre-Budget Report*, London: HMT

HMT (2007) *Budget 2007, Building Britain's long-term future: Prosperity and fairness for families*, London: HMT

HMT/Carbon Trust/DEFRA/Energy Saving Trust (2005) *Energy Efficiency Innovation Review: Household sector*, final report, London: HMT/Carbon Trust/DEFRA/EST

Holdsworth M (2003) *Green Choice, What Choice?*, London: National Consumer Council

Holdsworth M and Boyle D (2004) *Carrots Not Sticks: The possibilities of a sustainable consumption reward card for the UK*, London: NEF/NCC

Holdsworth M and Steadman P (2005) *16 Pain-Free Ways to Help Save the Planet*, London: NCC

Hounsham S (2006) *Painting the Town Green: How to persuade people to be environmentally friendly*, London: Green-Engage

House of Commons Environmental Audit Committee (2006) *Reducing Carbon Emissions from Transport*, ninth report of session 2005/06, volume 1, Norwich: The Stationery Office

House of Commons Transport Committee (2005) 'Finding a space for parking policy', press notice, 8 November, London: House of Commons

House of Lords Science and Technology Committee (2005) *Energy Efficiency: Volume 1*, London: The Stationery Office

Hurley S (2006) *The Public Ecology of Responsibility*, London: ippr, unpublished

Institute for European Environmental Policy (IEEP)/TNO /Centre for Automotive Industry Research (2005) *Service Contract to Carry out Economic Analysis and Business Impact Assessment of CO2 Emissions Reductions Measures in the Automotive Sector*, London: IEEP

Institute for Public Policy Research (ippr) (2005) *The Commission on Sustainable Development in the South-East*, final report, London: ippr

Jackson T (2005) *Motivating Sustainable Consumption: A review of evidence on consumer behaviour and behavioural change*, report to the Sustainable Development Research Network, Guildford: University of Surrey

Jackson T and Michaelis L (2003) *Policies for Sustainable Consumption*, report to the Sustainable Development Commission, Guildford/Oxford: University of Surrey/University of Oxford

Kollmuss A and Agyeman J (2002) 'Mind the gap: why do people act environmentally and what are the barriers to pro-environmental behaviour?' *Environmental Education Research*, vol 8 (3): 239–260

Lakoff G (2003) *Simple Framing: An introduction to framing and its uses in politics*, Berkeley: Rockridge Institute

Lane B (2005) *Car-buyer Research Report: Consumer attitudes to low-carbon and fuel-efficient passenger cars*, London: Ecolane Transport Consultancy/Low Carbon Vehicle Partnership

Leaman J (2004a) *Citizens want Tough Environmental Action Now*, London: MORI

Leaman J (2004b) *Saving the World Will Have to Wait, Most Americans Need Convincing*, London: MORI

Lees E (2006) *Evaluation of the Energy Efficiency Commitment 2002–05*, report by Eoin Lees Energy, London: DEFRA

Leggett J (2005) 'Please get serious about the survival technologies, solarcentury tells UK Government', news release, 2 November, London: solarcentury

Lippmann W (1921) *Public Opinion*, New York: The Free Press

Living Streets (2005) *Parking*, policy briefing 13, London: Living Streets

London Assembly (2005) *Power to the People: Renewable energy in Londoners' homes*, London: Environment Committee, London Assembly

London Borough of Merton (2007) 'List of boroughs', web resource, London: London Borough of Merton, available at: http://themertonrule.org/list-of-boroughs

Low Carbon Vehicle Partnership (LowCVP) (2006) 'UK's first E85 bioethanol filling pump opens', press release, 16 March 2006, London: LowCVP

Maiteny PT (2002) 'Mind the gap: summary of research exploring "inner" influences on pro-sustainable learning and behaviour', *Environmental Education Research*, vol 8 (3): 299–306

Market Transformation Programme (2005) *Sustainable Products 2005: Policy analysis and projections*, Didcot: MTP

Marshall G (2005) *Sleepwalking into Disaster: Are we in a state of denial about climate change?*,Oxford: Climate Outreach and Information Network, available at: http://coinet.org.uk/information/perspectives/marshall

Maslow A (1954) *Motivation and Personality*, New York: Harper

McCombs M (1994) 'News influence on our picture of the world', in Bryant J and Zillmann D (eds) *Media Effects: Advances in theory and research*, Hillsdale, NJ: Lawrence Erlbaum

McDonnell Social Norms Group (2006) 'Battling bad behaviour', *The Scientist*, vol 20 (2), 51–57

McKenzie-Mohr D (2000) 'Promoting sustainable behaviour: an introduction to community-based social marketing', *Journal of Social Issues*, vol 56 (3): 543–554

McKenzie-Mohr D and Smith W (1999) *Fostering Sustainable Behaviour: An introduction to community-based social marketing*, Gabriola Island, BC: New Society

Michaelis L (1997) *Special Issues in Carbon/Energy Taxation: Carbon charges on aviation fuels*, working paper 12 in the series Policies and Measures for Common Action Under the UNFCCC, Paris: OECD

Mitchell C and Woodman B (2004) *The Burning Question: Is the UK on course for a low carbon economy?* London: ippr

MORI (2005) *Congesting Charging*, London: MORI

MORI (2006) *MORI Delivery Index: Improving Public Services – Environment*, London: MORI

National Centre for Social Research (2006) 'British social attitudes data tables', web resource, London: NCSR, available at: www.britsocat.com

Natural Resources Defense Council (2005) *Eight Simple Rules for Talking about Global Warming*, Washington DC: NRDC

New Economics Foundation (2005) 'Behavioural economics: seven principles for policy-makers', in Dawnay E and Shah H *Theoretical New Economics 1*, London: New Economics Foundation

Nigbur D, Lyons E, Uzzell D and Muckle R (2005) *Increasing Recycling Through Community Action: Summary report of the Surrey Scholar Research Project to Guildford Borough Council*, Guildford: University of Surrey

Nordhaus T and Shellenberger M (2005) *Strategic Values Project*, Oakland, USA: American Environics

Norton A and Leaman J (2004) *The Day after Tomorrow: Public opinion on climate change*, London: MORI

O'Connor RE, Bord RJ and Fisher A (1999) 'Risk Perceptions, General Environmental Beliefs, and Willingness to Address Climate Change' *Journal of Risk Analysis* vol 19. (3): 461–471

ODPM (2001) *Planning Policy Guidance 13: Transport.* March 2001

ODPM (2004a) *Proposals for Amending Part L of the Building Regulations and Implementing the Energy Performance of Buildings Directive*, consultation document, London: ODPM

ODPM (2004b) *Planning Policy Statement 22: Renewable energy*, London: ODPM

ODPM (2005) *Proposals for Introducing a Code for Sustainable Homes: A consultation paper*, London: ODPM

ODPM (2006a) 'Live tables: Housing', web resource, London: ODPM, available at: www.odpm.gov.uk/index.asp?id=1156006

ODPM (2006b) 'More single households and growth in the Midlands and North increase housing demand', press release, 14 March 2006, London: ODPM

Office of National Statistics (ONS) (2005a) *Travel Trends 2004: A report on the International Passenger Survey*, Basingstoke: Palgrave Macmillan

Ofgem (2005a) *A Review of the Energy Efficiency Commitment 2002–2005*, report for the Secretary of State for Environment, Food and Rural Affairs, London: Ofgem

Ofgem (2005b) *The Energy Efficiency Commitment Briefing Paper*, London: Ofgem

Ofgem (2006) *Energy Efficiency Commitment Update 15*, London: Ofgem

ONS (2005b) 'National statistics: population estimates', web page, London: ONS, available at: www.statistics.gov.uk/CCI/nugget.asp?ID=6

ONS (2006) *Social Trends No 36*, Basingstoke: Palgrave Macmillan

Office of the Deputy Prime Minister (ODPM) (2001) *Planning Policy Guidance 13: Transport*, London: ODPM

Opinion Leader Research (OLR) (2003) *The New Persuaders: the changing nature of influence*, London: OLR

OLR (2005a) Public Consultation on Sustainable Development, London: DEFRA, unpublished

OLR (2005b) *Consumer Forum on Sustainable Consumption*, London: OLR

Oxera (2005) *Policies for Energy Efficiency in the UK Household Sector*, London: DEFRA

Pallak MS, Cook DA and Sullivan JJ (1980) 'Commitment and energy conservation' in Bickman L (ed), *Applied Social Psychology Annual*, Beverley Hills, CA: Sage

Palmer J and Boardman B (1998) *DELight Report*, Oxford: Environmental Change Institute

Park A, Curtice J, Thomson K, Jarvis L and Bromley C (eds) (2001) *British Social Attitudes: Public policy, social ties*, Aldershot: Dartmouth Publishing Company Ltd

Patent J and Lakoff G (2004) *Conceptual Levels: Bringing it home to values*, Berkeley: Rockridge Institute

Pavlov IP (1927) *Conditioned Reflexes*, London: Routledge and Kegan Paul

Performance and Innovation Unit (2002) *The Energy Review*, London: Performance and Innovation Unit, Cabinet Office

Petty R and Cacioppo J (1981) *Attitudes and Persuasion: Classic and contemporary approaches*, Dubuque, IA: William C Brown

Policy Studies Institute (2006) *A Green Living Initiative: Engaging households to achieve environmental goals*, London: Green Alliance

politics.co.uk (2006) Aviation tax 'unrealistic', web update, 7 February, available at: www.politics.co.uk/domestic-policy/aviation-tax-unrealistic-$15151158.htm

Poortinga W, Pidgeon N and Lorenzoni I (2006) *Public Perceptions of Nuclear Power, Climate Change and Energy Options in Britain: Summary findings of a survey conducted during October and November 2005*, Centre for Environmental Risk/University of East Anglia/Tyndall Centre for Climate Change Research

PricewaterhouseCoopers (PwC) (2005) *Sustainable Development in Government Fourth Annual Report 2005*, London: SDC

RAC (2006) *RAC Report on Motoring 2005: The agony and ecstasy of driving*, London: RAC, available at: www.rac.co.uk/web/racworld/issues/report_on_motoring/

RAC Foundation (2006) 'RAC Foundation welcomes launch of 'Drive Green Drive Safely', press release, 24 January 2006, London: RAC Foundation, available at: www.racfoundation.org/index.php?option=com_content&task=view&id=341&Itemid=35

Retallack S (2005) *Setting a Long-term Climate Objective*, report for the International Climate Change Taskforce, London: ippr

Rice R (2006) 'College drinking: norms vs. perceptions', *The Scientist*, vol 20 (2): 84–85

Rigby E, Harvey F and Birchall J (2007) 'Tesco to put "carbon rating" on labels', *Financial Times* January 18

Robbins T (2006) 'The great green rip-off?', *The Observer*, 10 December

Robbins T and Bowes G (2005) 'Escape news', *The Observer*, 27 November 2005: 5

Roberts S and Thumim J (2006) *A Rough Guide to Individual Carbon Trading: The ideas, the issues and the next steps*, London: DEFRA/Centre for Sustainable Energy

Rolls JM (2001) *A Review of Strategies Promoting Energy Related Behaviour Change*, Adelaide: Government of South Australia

Rose C (2004) *A Tool for Motivation Based Communication Strategy*, London: Campaign Strategy

Rose C, Dade P, Gallie N and Scott J (2005) *Climate Change Communications – Dipping a toe into public motivation*, London: Campaign Strategy

Sale Owen (2005) *Public Attitudes to Climate Change, Motivators and Barriers to Action: Newcastle and the North East*, London: Sale Owen

Schank R (1990) *Tell Me a Story: Narrative and intelligence*, Evanston: Northwestern University Press

Schellenberger M and Nordhaus T (2004) *The Death of Environmentalism: Global warming politics in a post-environmental world*, El Cerrito, CA: Breakthrough Institute

Scottish Executive (2006) *Cycling in Scotland 2005: TNS travel and tourism*, Edinburgh: Transport Research Planning Group

Shorrock LD and Utley JI (2003) *Domestic Energy Factfile 2003*, London: BRE

Simms A (2005) *Ecological Debt: The health of the planet and the wealth of nations*, London: Pluto Press

Sloman L (2006) *Car Sick: Solutions for our car-addicted culture*, London: Green Books

Slower Speeds Initiative (2006) Web page: http://www.slower-speeds.org.uk/content/view/100//

Society of Motor Manufacturers and Traders (SMMT) (2006a) *Safety First*, Tickbox.net survey, London: SMMT

SMMT (2006b) *Motor Industry Facts – 2006*, London: SMMT

SMMT (2006c) *UK New Car Registrations by CO_2 Performance: report on the 2005 market*, London: SMMT

Starkey R and Anderson K (2005) *Domestic Tradable Quotas: A policy instrument for reducing greenhouse gas emissions from energy use*, technical report 35, Norwich: Tyndall Centre for Climate Change Research

StarUK (2004) *UK Tourism Survey 2004*, StarUK

Steadman P (2005) *Desperately Seeking Sustainability?*, summary of National Consumer Council Research into information and advice on sustainable lifestyles, London: NCC

Steer Davies Gleave (2006) *Driving up Carbon Dioxide Emissions From Road Transport: An analysis of current government projections*, London: Transport 2000

Stoll-Kelleman S, O'Riordan T and Jaeger C (2001) 'The psychology of denial concerning climate mitigation measures: evidence from Swiss focus groups', *Global Environmental Change* vol 11: 107–117

Stradling S, Noble A, Carreno M, Jeffer G and Marshall I (2004) *Eight Reasons Why People Don't Like Buses*, Edinburgh: Transport Research Institute, Napier University

Sustainable Consumption Roundtable (SCR) (2005) *Seeing the Light: The impact of micro-generation on the way we use energy: qualitative research findings*, London: Hub Research Consultants/SCR

SCR (2006) *I Will if You Will: Towards sustainable consumption*, London: SCR

Sustainable Development Commission (SDC) (2005a) *Wind Power in the UK*, London: SDC

SDC (2005b) *Climate Change Programme Review: The submission of the Sustainable Development Commission*, London: SDC

SDC (2005c) *Leading by Example? Not exactly...* SEC commentary on the Sustainable Development in Government Report 2005, London: SDC

SDC (2005d) *Sustainable Buildings – The challenge of existing stock*, technical working paper, London: SDC

SDC (2006a) 'Lessons learned from white goods: how policy can create markets for greener products', presentation by Dr Stewart Davies to the CLGCC workshop, 11 April, London

SDC (2006b) *Stock Take: Delivering improvements in existing housing*, London: SDC

SDC/NCC (2005) *Seeing the Light: The impact of micro-generation on the way we use energy – Qualitative research findings*, London: SDC/NCC

Sustrans (2004) *Travel Behaviour Research Baseline Survey*, Bristol: Social Data/Sustrans

Thomas C (2004) *Public Attitudes and Behaviour in Western Riverside*, research study by the Open University/MORI Social Research Institute for Waste Watch, Rethink Rubbish Western Riverside, Yorkshire: Rethink Rubbish

Tools of Change (2007a) 'U-PASS: University of Washington's Transportation Management Program', web page, Ottawa: Cullbridge Marketing and Communications, available at: www.toolsofchange.com./English/CaseStudies/default.asp?Id=123

Tools of Change (2007b) 'Walking the talk?', web page, Ottawa: Cullbridge Marketing and Communications, available at: www.toolsofchange.com./English/CaseStudies/default.asp?Id=154

Transport 2000 (2006) 'Road schemes steal from public transport in regional carve-up of transport funding', press release, 10 February, London: Transport 2000

Transport for London (TfL) (2004a) *Central London Congestion Charging: Impacts monitoring*, second annual report, London: TfL

TfL (2004b) *Creating a Chain Reaction. The London Cycling Action Plan*, London: TfL

TfL (2005) *Central London Congestion Charging: Impacts monitoring*, third annual report, London: TfL

TfL (2006) *Central London Congestion Charging: Impacts monitoring*, fourth annual report, London: TfL

Transport Research Laboratory (2001) *A Quantitative Study of the Attitudes of Individuals to Cycling*, report 481, Wokingham: TRL

Trayner G (2006) *Open Source Thinking: From passive consumers to active creators*, London: Opinion Leader Research

United Nations Environment Programme (UNEP) (2005a) '2005 breaks a string of disastrous weather records', press release, 6 December, Nairobi: UNEP

UNEP (2005b) *Talk the Walk: Advancing sustainable lifestyles through marketing and communications,* Nairobi: UNEP

UNEP (2005c) *Communicating Sustainability: How to produce effective public campaigns,* Nairobi/London: UNEP/Futerra

UK Parliament (2006) *Climate Change and Sustainable Energy Act 2006,* London: The Stationery Office

Uzzell D (1999) 'Education for environmental action in the community: new roles and relationships', *Cambridge Journal of Education,* vol 29 (3): 397–413

Uzzell D (2000) 'The psycho-spatial dimension of global environmental problems', *Journal of Environmental Psychology* vol 20, 307–318

Vlek C, Reisch L and Scherhorn G (2000) *Transformation of Unsustainable Consumer Behaviours and Consumer Policies,* research report COV 00–04, Groningen, Netherlands: Centre for Environmental and Traffic Psychology, University of Groningen

Walk to School (2007) Website resources, available at: www.walktoschool.org.uk

Ward D (2007) 'Village on the road to a carbon-neutral future', *The Guardian,* 26 January

Waterson E (2005) *Changing Climate, Changing Behaviour. Delivering household energy saving through fiscal incentives,* London: EST

Watson J, Sauter R, Bakr B, James P, Myers L, and Wing R (2006) *Unlocking the Power House: Policy and system change for domestic micro-generation in the UK,* Brighton/Southampton/London: University of Sussex, Science Policy Research Unit/University of Southampton/Imperial College

Winhall J (2006) *Designing Future Public Services,* London: Design Council

World Health Organization (2005) *Climate and Health,* factsheet, Geneva: WHO

YouGov (2006) 'Survey results 30 October–1 November', London: YouGov/Daily Telegraph, available at: www.yougov.com

Appendix: Data on individuals' emissions

The data used to allocate emissions to UK individuals is from DEFRA's estimated emissions of carbon dioxide (CO_2 expressed as carbon) for 2004 (DEFRA 2006d, Table 5). 'End user' emission figures have been used where emissions from electricity generated in the power sector have been allocated pro rata to the respective consumers.

These calculations are approximate, and are based on numerous simplifying assumptions. It is not possible to provide a flawless breakdown to show which emissions individuals are directly responsible for, and the degree to which they exercise free choice in causing those emissions. Some simplifying assumptions have had to be made, due to the absence of necessary data. Emissions data is itself based on estimates, with inherent uncertainties.

However, as far as is reasonably practicable, these figures do give the breakdown of emissions for which UK citizens are directly responsible.

Domestic sector

All emissions from the domestic housing sector are the responsibility of the people who occupy domestic buildings, thus 100 per cent of emissions are assigned to individuals (Table 1).

Table 1: Breakdown of domestic-sector carbon emissions

Source breakdown	Percentage of sector[1]	Carbon attributable to individuals (MtC)
Total domestic	100	41.69
Space heating	56	23.35
Hot water	20	8.34
Cold appliances	6	2.50
Consumer electronics	3	1.25
Cooking	4	1.67
Lighting	6	2.50
Wet appliances	4	1.67
Miscellaneous	1	0.42

[1] Source of breakdown: SDC 2005d

Road-based transport

Not all vehicles on the road are used for personal travel, nor are all private vehicles used for purely non-business purposes. It has been assumed that approximately all light goods vehicles (LGVs) and heavy goods vehicles (HGVs) are used entirely commercially, for business purposes, and thus are not the responsibility of individuals. It has then been assumed that all cars, bus and motorbike emissions are the responsibility of individuals, except for a proportion of journeys used for business purposes.

The proportion of business-derived travel was determined from data on the distanced travelled per person by trip purpose in 2004, and not assigned to individuals' emissions (DfT 2005f) (Table 2).

Table 2: Breakdown of road-based transport carbon emissions

Source	Total emissions (MtC)	Percentage of sector[1]		Carbon attributable to individuals (MtC)	Percentage non-business -related travel[2]	Total individual emissions (MtC)
Total road	38.45	100		24.20	90	21.78
Car		59.61		22.92	90	20.63
Bus		2.96	62.93	1.14	90	1.02
Motorbike		0.36		0.14	90	0.12
LGVs		13.37		0.00	0	0.00
HGVs		23.24	37.07	0.00	0	0.00
Other		0.46		0.00	0	0.00

[1] Source: DEFRA 2006b, source category CO2 emission figures
[2] Source: DfT 2005f

The division of transport emissions by vehicle type was derived from DEFRA source category CO_2 emissions breakdowns for 2004, and then applied to the end-user emission figures proportionally.

Other transport
Rail transport was broken down into emissions from passenger journeys and emissions from freight transport, using the number of kilometres travelled by passengers and by freight (personal communication from DfT to authors, 2006).

Emissions caused by business travel were then removed from the passenger share of emissions, to leave what was attributable to an individual's lifestyle choice. The breakdown on the purpose of travel was based on the distanced travelled per person, by trip purpose, in 2004 (DfT 2005f).

No figures are available to calculate the proportion of freight and passenger travel by water within the UK. Transport via water makes up a very small amount of total transport emissions (2.6 per cent). Given the uncertainties and approximations made in other areas, and the likelihood that freight travel dominates, no emissions from water-related travel have been assigned to individuals.

Table 3: Breakdown of other transport carbon emissions

Source	Total emissions (MtC)	Percentage of sector	Percentage passenger vs. freight[1]	Carbon attributable to individuals (MtC)	Percentage non-business -related travel[2]	Total individual emissions (MtC)
Total other	2.92	100				1.16
Rail	1.82	62.3	70.8	1.29	90	1.16
Water	1.1	37.7	Data Unavailable			0

[1] Source: Personal communication from DfT to authors, 2006
[2] Source: DfT 2005f

Aviation

All domestic flights have been presumed to be taken by UK citizens. The number of trips made by visitors to the UK, and by residents of the UK, was used to assign emissions from international aviation to UK citizens (ONS 2005a). Data on the distance travelled per trip, and by residency or purpose, is not widely available, and thus the proportioning of emissions is not perfect but reflects a best possible estimate.

Most freight (63 per cent) is carried in the hold of passenger aircraft (Civil Aviation Authority 2004, Table 6). The total number of flights made by cargo aircraft represents 3.3 per cent of all aircraft activity, with the remainder being made by passenger aircraft (ibid). Using these figures, emissions from freight transport have been removed from an individual's contribution.

The proportion of non-business flights was derived from the number of trips, by purpose (ONS 2005a). Due to limitations in data, it is not possible to determine these breakdowns in relation to the distance flown, and thus the precise quantity of emissions created per trip.

Table 4: Breakdown of aviation carbon emissions

Source	Total emissions (MtC)	Percentage of sector[1]	Percentage passenger vs. freight	Percentage UK citizens[2]	Carbon attributable to UK individuals (MtC)	Percentage non-business related travel[2]	Total individual emissions (MtC)
Total aviation	10.84	100	96.7				6.48
Domestic	1.81	16.7		100	1.75	60	1.05
International	9.03	83.3		71.6	6.25	86.9	5.43

[1] Source: Personal communication from DfT to authors, 2006
[2] Source: ONS 2005

Per-capita emissions

UK individuals were collectively responsible for 71.12 million tonnes of carbon-equivalent (MtCe) (260.76 MtCO$_2$) of CO$_2$ emissions in 2004 (43.6 per cent of total CO$_2$ emissions). In 2004, the UK had an estimated population of 59,834,300 people (ONS 2005b). So it can be estimated that an individual UK citizen would have been directly responsible for approximately 1.19 tC or 4.36 tCO$_2$ in 2004.